**Improve your bridge game—
the entertaining way.**

♠

All the puzzles in this book contain hands that you
might hold in your next game.

♥

Tackle them as though you were sitting around a
bridge table and could see only your own hand.
Then bid and play as both declarer and defender.

♦

Not only will you have fun, but you'll learn a great
deal about bridge in the process.

♣

**DEVYN PRESS BOOK OF BRIDGE PUZZLES #3
(Originally Titled "Pocket Book of Bridge Puzzles #3")**

DEVYN PRESS BOOK OF BRIDGE PUZZLES #3 IS A REPRINT OF THE
POCKET BOOK OF BRIDGE PUZZLES #3
Pocket Book edition published June, 1970
DEVYN PRESS EDITION PUBLISHED JANUARY, 1981

PRINTED IN THE UNITED STATES OF AMERICA

Manufactured in the U.S.A.
    Devyn Press
    1327 Walnut St.
    Shelbyville, KY 40065

DEVYN PRESS BOOK OF

BRIDGE PUZZLES

NUMBER

3

by Alfred Sheinwold

(Originally Titled Pocket Book Of Bridge Puzzles #3)

Devyn Press
Shelbyville, Kentucky

Cover by
Bonnie J. Baron

Introduction

If this is your first encounter with one of my bridge puzzle books, I hope you will go back to your bookshop and camp on the cash register until they sell you Book 1 and Book 2. But first, a word of explanation to help you enjoy these puzzles.

Tackle each deal as though it were dealt out in your regular bridge game. Put yourself in each player's place in turn, beginning with the dealer. Imagine what you would bid at each turn if you could see only that player's hand. Try not to peek because you will miss part of the fun if you do. (Actually you can't help peeking because you have to look at each hand to work out the bidding; but try not to base your bidding on the fact that you can see all of the cards.) See if you can work out the same bidding that appears at the top of the right-hand page of each puzzle. The players use what is often called "Standard American" bidding methods, with Blackwood and Stayman but no other fancy conventions. The fact that South always plays the hand as declarer may give you a clue to the "right" contract.

When you have decided on the right bids for each player, write them at the bottom of the hand—in the spaces provided for this. Pick West's best opening lead also—not a "peeking" opening lead, but the lead he would probably make if he could see only his own hand. Then write that down.

Now you can try to play the hand. Take a light pencil and draw a slim slanting line through each card as you play it. Don't act with a knowledge of all four hands; assume that each player can see only his own hand and the dummy—just as in an actual game. Declarer should usually make his contract by proper play—but, since you are both declarer and defender, always try to defeat the contract by logical play.

Take the hand on this page, for example. Let's assume that you got to three notrump by some logical bidding and that you chose the actual opening lead of the jack of hearts. Take the play from that point on.

East dealer   **Both sides vulnerable**

NORTH
♠ K Q
♡ A 6 3
◇ J 4
♣ A J 9 7 5 3

WEST
♠ A J 8
♡ K J 10 8 7
◇ K 9 8 2
♣ 2

EAST-D
♠ 7 6 5 4
♡ 9 5 2
◇ Q 6 5
♣ Q 10 8

SOUTH
♠ 10 9 3 2
♡ Q 4
◇ A 10 7 3
♣ K 6 4

EAST	SOUTH	WEST	NORTH
Pass	Pass	1 ♡	2 ♣
Pass	3 ♣	Pass	3 ♡
Pass	3 NT	All Pass	

Opening lead — ♡ J

Draw a slanting line through West's lead of the jack of hearts and through North's lowest heart; then through East's deuce of hearts and South's queen.

So far, so good. You have won the first trick with the queen of hearts. Should South go after the clubs next? They will surely furnish the bulk of declarer's tricks.

Try this for a few tricks, drawing a slanting line through each card as it is played. You will have to give up a club trick to East, and he will return a heart, forcing out dummy's ace. You will be able to win five clubs, one diamond and two hearts—for a total of eight tricks.

The moment South leads a spade, West will take the ace of spades and will defeat the contract with the rest of the hearts.

"Well," you say to yourself, "that's probably the point of this hand. The defense is supposed to beat three notrump by plugging away at hearts each time they get in."

Then you would look at the right-hand page of the puzzle to see how the hand was played. And you would discover that South should make three notrump against the best defense.

But first, you might take a look at the "right" bidding. Notice that North does not bid three notrump himself. Instead, he makes a cue-bid in hearts, inviting South to bid notrump if he can supply an additional stopper or the makings of a stopper. *North* would go down against the normal heart opening lead by East; but *South* makes three notrump because the heart lead by West gives South a second heart trick.

Now for the "correct" way for South to play the hand. South knows he will surely get nine tricks if the clubs behave themselves. South also knows that now and then a club suit breaks badly. What can he do to guard against the sort of club break that actually exists?

After winning the first trick with the queen of hearts, South must immediately lead a *spade*. Pick up your pencil again and draw a circle around each card as it is played in this second version of the play.

West takes the ace of spades (draw a ring around the ace of spades) and returns the king of hearts. *Let West win this trick*—but take the next heart trick. Now you can safely go after the clubs, allowing East to win the second or third club with the queen. East cannot lead a heart for a very good reason: He has none left.

No matter what East does, you can get to dummy with the king of spades to run the rest of the clubs. You make your game despite the bad club break.

Some players prefer to skip play of the hand based on their own bidding. Instead, after working out their own bidding, they turn to the bidding at the top of the right-hand page and use the opening lead shown there. *Then* they proceed with their own play of the hand by making a slanting line as each trick is played. When the hand is over, they read what happened in the hand. Do it whichever way you prefer.

Now you are ready for the puzzles. How wonderful it must be to see these hands for the first time!

ALFRED SHEINWOLD

3

Improbable Break Is Not Impossible

We've been trying to get a bill through Congress to wipe out the difference between the improbable and the impossible, but you know what Congress is like. We'll have to struggle along for another year or two with an occasional bad break in a key suit.

South dealer   **North-South vulnerable**

NORTH
♠ 10 9
♡ K J 9 5 3
♢ Q J
♣ Q J 4 2

WEST   EAST
♠ K Q 8 2   ♠ J 7 6 4 3
♡ 7 6   ♡ Q 10 8 4 2
♢ 9 8 6 2   ♢ A
♣ 9 8 5   ♣ 7 6

SOUTH-D
♠ A 5
♡ A
♢ K 10 7 5 4 3
♣ A K 10 3

Defense Tricks:

☐ ☐ ☐ ☐ ☐ ☐ ☐ ☐ ☐ ☐ ☐ ☐ ☐ ☐

Bid the hand your way:

North	East	South	West
_____	_____	_____	_____
_____	_____	_____	_____
_____	_____	_____	_____
_____	_____	_____	_____

Opening Lead _____

4

How the hand was bid:

SOUTH	WEST	NORTH	EAST
1 ◇	Pass	1 ♡	Pass
2 ♣	Pass	3 ♣	Pass
6 ♣	All Pass		

Opening lead — ♠ K

How the hand was played: Imagine you're South. You take the ace of spades, cash the ace of hearts and plan to reach dummy and discard a spade on the king of hearts.

You draw trumps with the ace, the queen and the jack. Now you cash the king of hearts to get rid of a spade and lead the queen of diamonds to force out the ace.

Back comes a spade, and you must ruff with your last trump. But all of your lovely aces have gone. You cannot cash the jack of diamonds and get back to your hand.

ONLY CHANCE

Your only chance is to lead the king of diamonds, overtaking dummy's jack. This will work out well if the diamonds break 3-2, as they should about two-thirds of the time.

As it happens, the diamonds break 4-1. You cannot run the suit, and you wind up going down two. Get ready to send a letter to your senator.

Don't be surprised if your senator tells you that you should have played the hand better. The correct line is to draw only two rounds of trumps before cashing the king of hearts and leading the queen of diamonds from dummy.

When a spade comes back, you ruff; but you still have a trump left in your hand. You can lead a diamond to dummy's jack and still get back with your high trump to draw West's last trump and run all of the diamonds.

Suppose that second diamond gets ruffed? That won't happen if the diamonds break 3-2. It also won't happen if the player with one diamond started with only two trumps.

Be Sure You're Awake When out of Bed

"Every card was wrong, partner," said South after he had finished playing the hand shown below. "Some days it doesn't pay to get out of bed." And with that profound thought he cut the cards for the next deal.

South dealer   **Both sides vulnerable**

```
                    NORTH
                    ♠ K 5 4 2
                    ♡ K 10 7 5
                    ◇ 6 5 2
                    ♣ 10 4

         WEST                      EAST
         ♠ Q 10 9 7                ♠ 6 3
         ♡ 3                       ♡ Q 8
         ◇ A Q 3                   ◇ J 10 9 8 4
         ♣ A 8 6 5 3               ♣ J 9 7 2

                    SOUTH-D
                    ♠ A J 8
                    ♡ A J 9 6 4 2
                    ◇ K 7
                    ♣ K Q
```

Defense Tricks:

☐ ☐ ☐ ☐ ☐ ☐ ☐ ☐ ☐ ☐ ☐ ☐

Bid the hand your way:

North	East	South	West
_____	_____	_____	_____
_____	_____	_____	_____
_____	_____	_____	_____
_____	_____	_____	_____

Opening Lead _____

How the hand was bid:

SOUTH	WEST	NORTH	EAST
1 ♡	Double	2 ♡	Pass
4 ♡	All Pass		

Opening lead — ♣ A

How the hand was played: West opened the ace of clubs and continued with a club to South's king. Declarer led a heart to dummy's king and drew another trump with the ace. So far, so good.

South's next step was to lead a spade to the king and a spade back for a finesse with the jack. This lost to the queen, and back came a spade to the ace.

The spades failed to break, and South eventually led a trump to dummy for a diamond return. The ace of diamonds captured the king, and South lost another diamond.

SHOULD MAKE CONTRACT

It's true that all the cards were wrong, but South should still make the contract. After drawing trumps South should lead a trump to dummy's ten and return a low spade. When East plays a low spade, South should play the eight.

West is forced to win the trick. If West returns a spade, South gets a free finesse and can get back with a trump to discard a diamond on the king of spades. If West returns a diamond instead of a spade, South wins a trick with the king of diamonds. If West returns a club, dummy ruffs and South discards a diamond.

Even if East had the nine of spades, he could not interfere with the plan. If East puts up the nine of spades on the first round of spades, South covers with the jack. West can win with the queen, but then a spade return will still give South a free finesse.

Even on a day when most things go wrong, it may still pay to get out of bed if you wake yourself up.

7

Lawyer Plays Bridge with Two-Fold Plan

A good lawyer always has two strings to his bow. "My client was a thousand miles away when the murder was committed," he will argue. "And anyway, it was self-defense." Burt Marks, who proved to the California Supreme Court that bridge is a game of skill, not only argues that way—he plays a hand two ways at once.

North dealer   **Both sides vulnerable**

NORTH-D
♠ A 7 3
♡ A 9 2
♢ A J 9 7 3
♣ 5 2

WEST
♠ K 10 6 2
♡ 10 6 5
♢ 6 4 2
♣ A J 9

EAST
♠ Q 9 8 4
♡ 4
♢ Q 10 8 5
♣ K 10 8 7

SOUTH
♠ J 5
♡ K Q J 8 7 3
♢ K
♣ Q 6 4 3

Defense Tricks:

☐ ☐ ☐ ☐ ☐ ☐ ☐ ☐ ☐ ☐ ☐ ☐ ☐

Bid the hand your way:

North	East	South	West
_____	_____	_____	_____
_____	_____	_____	_____
_____	_____	_____	_____
_____	_____	_____	_____
		Opening Lead	_____

How the hand was bid:

NORTH	EAST	SOUTH	WEST
1 ◊	Pass	1 ♡	Pass
1 NT	Pass	4 ♡	All Pass
			Opening lead — ♡ 5

How the hand was played: West opened the five of hearts and Marks won in his hand. He was sure of six trumps, two aces and the king of diamonds. He needed only one other trick to score game and rubber.

One way to play the hand was to try for a club ruff in dummy. But persistent trump leads by West would clear the trumps out of dummy and prevent a ruff.

Another plan was to set up one of dummy's diamonds by ruffing. But there might not be enough entries to dummy.

TRIES BOTH

Marks tried both plans at once. He cashed the king of diamonds and led a low club.

If West failed to return a heart, declarer would have time to ruff a club in dummy. For example, if West returned a spade, declarer would put up dummy's ace and return a club. Then nothing could stop a club ruff.

If West returned a heart, dummy's nine would be a safe entry to dummy. (If West led a heart and East could play the ten of hearts, South would win and then dummy's last trump could not be knocked out to prevent a club ruff.) Then declarer could cash the ace of diamonds, ruff a diamond, get back with the ace of hearts to ruff another diamond and finally get back with the ace of spades to cash the last diamond.

You don't have to be a lawyer to play a hand with two plans in mind. This type is especially common: Try for the long suit while you're aiming at a ruffing trick. If you don't get one, the other may come through.

Safe Round of Trumps Loses Slam

There is such a thing as playing a hand so safe that you go down. One good way of doing this is to draw a premature round of trumps.

South dealer   **Both sides vulnerable**

NORTH
- ♠ 10 8 3
- ♡ None
- ◇ K Q J 10 9 5
- ♣ A 10 7 4

WEST
- ♠ 6 4 2
- ♡ A K J 9 6 5 2
- ◇ A 6 2
- ♣ None

EAST
- ♠ K J 9 5
- ♡ 7 3
- ◇ 8 7 4 3
- ♣ J 3 2

SOUTH-D
- ♠ A Q 7
- ♡ Q 10 8 4
- ◇ None
- ♣ K Q 9 8 6 5

Defense Tricks:

☐ ☐ ☐ ☐ ☐ ☐ ☐ ☐ ☐ ☐ ☐ ☐ ☐

Bid the hand your way:

North	East	South	West
___	___	___	___
___	___	___	___
___	___	___	___
___		___	___
		Opening Lead ___	

How the hand was bid:

SOUTH	WEST	NORTH	EAST
1 ♣	1 ♡	2 ◇	Pass
3 ♣	3 ♡	4 ♡	Pass
4 ♠	Pass	6 ♣	All Pass

Opening lead — ♡ K

How the hand was played: West led the king of hearts, and declarer quite properly ruffed in dummy. Then, "for safety's sake," declarer led dummy's seven of clubs to his own king.

West discarded a heart, and South suddenly found the room uncomfortably warm. It's strange how the perspiration comes out when you've just tossed away a vulnerable slam.

South ruffed a heart with dummy's ten of clubs and led the king of diamonds from dummy, discarding the queen of hearts from his hand.

West took the ace of diamonds and considered a shift to spades. Just in time, however, West remembered that East had played the seven of hearts at the first trick and the three of hearts on the next round of the suit.

TRUSTS PARTNER

Trusting his partner, West led the ace of hearts, forcing declarer to ruff in dummy with the ace of trumps. Now East was sure to win the setting trick with the jack of clubs.

South should make the slam by leading the king of diamonds from dummy at the second trick. Declarer discards a low heart, and West wins with the ace of diamonds.

West can make things difficult only by returning the ace of hearts. South ruffs in dummy and draws two rounds of trumps with the king and ace. He can then discard two spades on the queen and jack of diamonds to make sure of the slam.

11

Maneuver Is Not Indelicate

About forty years ago, Milton C. Work wanted to write about a bridge maneuver called "stripping." Some of his newspapers considered this term indelicate, so Work solved the problem by calling the maneuver "elimination." As you can see in a simple example, the maneuver itself is not at all indelicate.

North dealer   **North-South vulnerable**

NORTH-D

♠ 6 3
♡ K 5 4 3
◇ K 10 4
♣ A K 7 4

WEST	EAST
♠ K 10 9 8 5 2	♠ 7 4
♡ 8 2	♡ A 7
◇ A 2	◇ 9 8 6 5 3
♣ Q J 2	♣ 10 9 8 5

SOUTH

♠ A Q J
♡ Q J 10 9 6
◇ Q J 7
♣ 6 3

Defense Tricks:

☐ ☐ ☐ ☐ ☐ ☐ ☐ ☐ ☐ ☐ ☐ ☐ ☐

Bid the hand your way:

North	East	South	West
_____	_____	_____	_____
_____	_____	_____	_____
_____	_____	_____	_____
_____	_____	_____	_____
		Opening Lead	_____

How the hand was bid:

NORTH	EAST	SOUTH	WEST
1 ♣	Pass	1 ♡	1 ♠
2 ♡	Pass	3 NT	Pass
4 ♡	All Pass		

Opening lead — ◊ A

How the hand was played: West leads the ace of diamonds and then a low diamond. South is thus threatened with a diamond ruff in addition to the two aces and the king of spades.

Most players would go ahead with the trumps anyway, relying on the spade finesse to see them through. East takes the first trump with the ace and returns a diamond for West to ruff.

West gets out safely with a club, and South must eventually try the spade finesse. Down one.

WORKS ON CLUBS

South can make the contract by working on the clubs before drawing trumps. (And there's a phrase that not even the most delicate person could sniff at.)

After winning the second trick, declarer cashes the top clubs and ruffs a club in his hand. This strips the clubs from West's hand. Or you might say it eliminates the clubs from the West hand.

Now South leads a trump. East wins with the ace of trumps and leads a diamond for West to ruff.

What does West lead now? He has nothing but spades, so he must give South a free finesse. South gratefully takes his two spade tricks and ruffs a spade in dummy, winning the game and rubber.

Don't Despise Lowly Trump

It's very hard to think respectfully of a dime when your wallet is full of hundred-dollar bills. If you're willing to take this risk, consider the fate of South in this hand.

North dealer   **Both sides vulnerable**

NORTH-D
- ♠ A 8 6 3
- ♡ 5
- ◇ 9 4
- ♣ A K Q J 8 3

WEST	EAST
♠ 9 2	♠ K Q 10 7
♡ 8 7 3 2	♡ 9 6
◇ A K Q J 7 3	◇ 10 6
♣ 6	♣ 10 9 5 4 2

SOUTH
- ♠ J 5 4
- ♡ A K Q J 10 4
- ◇ 8 5 2
- ♣ 7

Defense Tricks:

☐ ☐ ☐ ☐ ☐ ☐ ☐ ☐ ☐ ☐ ☐ ☐ ☐

Bid the hand your way:

North	East	South	West
_____	_____	_____	_____
_____	_____	_____	_____
_____	_____	_____	_____
_____	_____	_____	_____
		Opening Lead	_____

How the hand was bid:

NORTH	EAST	SOUTH	WEST
1 ♣	Pass	1 ♡	2 ◇
3 ♣	Pass	4 ♡	All Pass

Opening lead — ◇ K

How the hand was played: West won the first two tricks with the king and jack of diamonds. East signalled with the ten and six, instructing his partner to continue.

West continued with the queen of diamonds, and South disdainfully played dummy's lowly five of trumps. South had no real respect for dummy's tiny trump.

Of course you can see what happened. South lost the game and rubber by wasting dummy's tiny trump. Make no mistake about it: Contract bridge is a game with a moral in each and every hand!

RETURNS SPADE

East overruffed with the six of hearts, winning the third defensive trick. Then East returned the king of spades.

South took dummy's ace of spades and started on the clubs, hoping to get rid of two spades safely.

West ruffed the second club and led a spade to his partner's queen. South was down two, thus winding up with a minus score of 50 points despite his trump honors.

Now go back to the third trick and see what happens if South should discard from dummy any black card except the ace of spades.

The defenders thus win the first three tricks, but there they end. When they next lead a spade to dummy's ace (best defense), declarer can lead dummy's low trump to reach his hand and draw the rest of the trumps. Then South leads his club to dummy to get rid of two spades on high clubs.

Think Right Thoughts When Squeezing

Most bridge players think of a squeeze as a way of forcing an opponent to discard a winning card. It is possible, however, to have something else in mind when you begin to squeeze somebody. For example, you may simply want to lock all the doors.

South dealer   **Both sides vulnerable**

NORTH
♠ A Q
♡ 10 4
◇ J 10 5 3 2
♣ A 10 9 6

WEST
♠ 9 6 5 3 2
♡ Q 8 6 5 2
◇ None
♣ 8 3 2

EAST
♠ 10 8 7 4
♡ K J 3
◇ A Q 9 8
♣ 7 4

SOUTH-D
♠ K J
♡ A 9 7
◇ K 7 6 4
♣ K Q J 5

Defense Tricks:

☐ ☐ ☐ ☐ ☐ ☐ ☐ ☐ ☐ ☐ ☐ ☐ ☐ ☐ ☐

Bid the hand your way:

North	East	South	West
_____	_____	_____	_____
_____	_____	_____	_____
_____	_____	_____	_____
_____	_____	_____	_____
		Opening Lead _____	

How the hand was bid:

SOUTH	WEST	NORTH	EAST
1 NT	Pass	3 NT	All Pass

Opening lead — ♡ 5

How the hand was played: When this hand came along in a recent San Francisco Regional Tournament, Mike McMahon, winner of the Open Pair Championship, held off his ace of hearts until the third trick. Then he led a club to dummy's ten and a low diamond to his own king.

It was a good idea since the hand was hopeless if West had the ace of diamonds. Nothing could stop South if East had two or three diamonds headed by the ace.

When West discarded a spade, however, McMahon had to stop and make a new plan. Four diamonds in the East hand were too much of a good thing.

SEEMED IMPOSSIBLE

It seemed impossible to develop another diamond trick since East still had A-Q-9 behind dummy's J-10. McMahon thought of a squeeze play and ran the rest of his clubs.

East had to make two discards. If East threw a diamond, McMahon could give up a diamond, win the spade return, give up another diamond and then take a spade and an established diamond.

Since East couldn't afford to throw a diamond, he had to part with two spades. This cut off his escape.

McMahon promptly cashed his two spades, reducing East to his three diamonds. Then he led the jack of diamonds. East could take the queen and ace of diamonds but had to yield the last trick to dummy's ten of diamonds.

Now you will think the right thoughts when you plan to squeeze somebody.

Disregard Book Rule to Make Slam

Everybody knows how to play Q-2 opposite A-K-6. You win the first trick with the queen, because this leaves you in position to win the next two tricks with the ace and king. Life would be very simple if you could always depend on the book rules to work.

South dealer   **Both sides vulnerable**

NORTH
♠ 8 7 6 2
♡ Q 2
◇ A 4
♣ Q 9 7 6 2

WEST   EAST
♠ 10 4 3   ♠ 9
♡ J 10 9 5   ♡ 8 7 4 3
◇ K 8 3 2   ◇ J 10 9 6
♣ 5 3   ♣ K J 10 8

SOUTH-D
♠ A K Q J 5
♡ A K 6
◇ Q 7 5
♣ A 4

Defense Tricks:

☐ ☐ ☐ ☐ ☐ ☐ ☐ ☐ ☐ ☐ ☐ ☐ ☐

Bid the hand your way:

North	East	South	West
_____	_____	_____	_____
_____	_____	_____	_____
_____	_____	_____	_____
_____	_____	_____	_____

Opening Lead _____

How the hand was bid:

SOUTH	WEST	NORTH	EAST
2 ♠	Pass	3 ♠	Pass
4 ♣	Pass	4 ◊	Pass
4 ♡	Pass	4 ♠	Pass
6 ♠	All Pass		

Opening lead — ♡ J

How the hand was played: In this case, South relied on the rule and won the first trick in dummy with the queen of hearts. This cost him his slam contract.

He drew three rounds of trumps, cashed the ace of clubs and gave up a club trick. Back came the jack of diamonds, covered by the queen and king and won by dummy's ace.

South ruffed a club, but the suit failed to break. He cashed the top hearts, discarding a diamond from dummy, ruffed a diamond in dummy and ruffed another club.

Now dummy's last club was good, but there was no way to reach it. South had to lose a diamond trick.

ADDITIONAL ENTRY

South can make the contract by keeping an additional entry in dummy. He wins the first heart trick with the king, draws three rounds of trumps, cashes the ace of clubs and gives up a club.

East returns a diamond to dummy's ace, and South ruffs a club. South leads a heart to dummy's queen (saved there for just this purpose) and ruffs another club.

Now South cashes the ace of hearts to discard the low diamond from dummy. And it is then easy to win the last two tricks in dummy with the last trump and the last club.

The point is that you must manage your entries not merely for the sake of a suit but for the sake of the hand as a whole.

Appearances Count More Than Reality

In a certain kind of hand, where appearances are just as important as reality, the master of illusion is the star. For example, in a recent all-expert game, the outstanding play of the session was made by Billy Wilder, famous motion-picture writer-director.

South dealer   **North-South vulnerable**

NORTH
- ♠ 10 6 5 3
- ♡ K J 6 3
- ◊ 9 5
- ♣ K 7 4

WEST
- ♠ 8 7 4
- ♡ Q 4
- ◊ K J 8 6 4
- ♣ Q J 10

EAST
- ♠ 2
- ♡ A 10 9 8 7 2
- ◊ A Q 10 3
- ♣ 6 3

SOUTH-D
- ♠ A K Q J 9
- ♡ 5
- ◊ 7 2
- ♣ A 9 8 5 2

Defense Tricks:

☐ ☐ ☐ ☐ ☐ ☐ ☐ ☐ ☐ ☐ ☐ ☐ ☐ ☐

Bid the hand your way:

North	East	South	West
___	___	___	___
___	___	___	___
___	___	___	___
___	___	___	___
		Opening Lead ___	

How the hand was bid:

SOUTH	WEST	NORTH	EAST
1 ♠	Pass	2 ♠	3 ♡
4 ♠	All Pass		

Opening lead — ♡ Q

How the hand was played: South should lose a heart, two diamonds and a club, but don't let this reality depress you. Years of working at the side of the camera have taught Wilder that the left hand knoweth not what the right hand doeth.

Wilder saw that he would be showing the wrong profile if he covered the opening lead with dummy's king of hearts. East would win with the ace of hearts and shift to dummy's weakness — diamonds. The defenders would take their two diamond tricks and would eventually get a club to defeat the contract.

OTHER PROFILE

Wilder decided to keep the outer cheek turned to the opponents. He played a low heart from dummy at the first trick, allowing West to win the trick.

Things looked different from West's angle. West didn't relish leading a diamond through dummy's weakness. Instead, he led the queen of clubs through dummy's strength.

This was just what Wilder had been angling for. He won with the ace of clubs, drew three rounds of trumps ending in dummy and led the king of hearts through East. Up came the ace of hearts, and Wilder ruffed.

Declarer got back to dummy with the king of clubs to discard a diamond on the jack of hearts. Then he could give up a club to set up his long suit. The defenders got only one diamond, and Wilder made game and rubber.

Take Right View of Bridge Foes

Much as it may go against your principles, think of your opponents as dogs. Expect them to bark when the time for barking comes. Be warned of danger if they don't bark when any self-respecting dog would yap like crazy.

South dealer　　　　　　　　　　　**Both sides vulnerable**

NORTH
- ♠ J 10 9 8 5
- ♡ 6 2
- ◇ K J 5
- ♣ Q 10 6

WEST
- ♠ 6 4
- ♡ A K J 9 7 3
- ◇ 8 7
- ♣ 9 4 3

EAST
- ♠ 3
- ♡ Q 5
- ◇ Q 10 9 4 3
- ♣ K J 8 5 2

SOUTH-D
- ♠ A K Q 7 2
- ♡ 10 8 4
- ◇ A 6 2
- ♣ A 7

Defense Tricks:

☐ ☐ ☐ ☐ ☐ ☐ ☐ ☐ ☐ ☐ ☐ ☐ ☐

Bid the hand your way:

North	East	South	West
‾‾‾	‾‾‾	‾‾‾	‾‾‾
‾‾‾	‾‾‾	‾‾‾	‾‾‾
‾‾‾	‾‾‾	‾‾‾	‾‾‾
‾‾‾	‾‾‾	‾‾‾	‾‾‾
		Opening Lead ‾‾‾	

How the hand was bid:

SOUTH	WEST	NORTH	EAST
1 ♠	Pass	2 ♠	Pass
4 ♠	All Pass		

Opening lead — ♡ K

How the hand was played: West led the king of hearts, continued with the ace and then led the jack to make dummy ruff.

Declarer, a respectable type who wouldn't think of a dog even if he fell over a hydrant, drew trumps, cashed the ace of clubs and led a low club toward dummy. West naturally played low, and South thought he was doing his full duty by wondering whether to play the queen or the ten of clubs from dummy.

It didn't actually matter. South had already flubbed the hand. East could win the trick and got out with a high club to make South ruff again. Eventually South would lose a diamond trick for a score of minus 100 points.

GOOD MATERIAL

The play to the first three tricks showed that West started with a very strong six-card heart suit. This was very good yelping material, so why did West keep quiet?

Clearly West had nothing else to bark about. East surely held the queen of diamonds and the king of clubs.

If South came to this correct conclusion, he could make the contract. After drawing trumps, South should lead out the top diamonds and give East his diamond trick. East must then lead away from his king of clubs, so that South avoids the loss of a club trick.

Policeman Detects Skulking

A policeman is trained to look for suspicious behavior. He pays no attention to people who are walking in a normal manner; he jumps into action if he sees somebody skulking along. A good bridge policeman must be ready to skewer the skulker at the bridge table.

South dealer   **East-West vulnerable**

```
                        NORTH
                        ♠ K 10 7
                        ♡ Q 6
                        ◇ Q J 10 5 4
                        ♣ 9 3 2

        WEST                              EAST
        ♠ A 8 3                           ♠ 9 6 5 2
        ♡ K J 10 9 7                      ♡ 8 4 3
        ◇ A 6                             ◇ 9 3
        ♣ Q J 7                           ♣ 10 8 5 4

                        SOUTH-D
                        ♠ Q J 4
                        ♡ A 5 2
                        ◇ K 8 7 2
                        ♣ A K 6
```

Defense Tricks:

☐ ☐ ☐ ☐ ☐ ☐ ☐ ☐ ☐ ☐ ☐ ☐ ☐

Bid the hand your way:

North	East	South	West
____	____	____	____
____	____	____	____
____	____	____	____
		____	____

Opening Lead _____

24

How the hand was bid:

SOUTH	WEST	NORTH	EAST
1 NT	Pass	2 NT	Pass
3 NT	Double	All Pass	

Opening lead — ♡ J

How the hand was played: West led the jack of hearts, and South breathed more comfortably when dummy's queen held the first trick. Unfortunately for him, he was still not home.

If South went after diamonds, he would win four diamonds, two hearts and two clubs. West, who surely had both missing aces for his double, would take the ace of diamonds and knock out the ace of hearts.

South couldn't make his contract by force so decided to see how far he could get by stealth. He therefore led a club to his hand and returned the jack of spades toward dummy.

OBVIOUS SKULDUGGERY

This was an obvious bit of skulduggery. West should have said to himself: "What can the wretch be doing with spades? Why isn't he work on the diamonds like a normal human being?"

From this kind of alert questioning, it would be just a step to putting up the ace of spades. West would then knock out the ace of hearts. South would have to lead diamonds very soon, and then West would take the ace of diamonds and the hearts.

When the hand was actually played, West foolishly played a low spade on South's jack—hoping that South was about to take a losing finesse to a queen that East couldn't possibly hold.

This allowed South to steal one spade trick. Now he could switch to diamonds and run nine tricks.

Make Right Wish to Win

Once upon a time there was a poor but honest bridge player who seemed never to win a finesse. He complained so bitterly that the gods of luck sent a special messenger down to grant him a successful finesse. "Give him whatever he asks for," were the messenger's instructions. "Just get him to shut up."

South dealer   **Neither side vulnerable**

NORTH
♠ 8 7 4 2
♡ A 10 9
◇ 7 5 2
♣ 8 5 4

WEST   EAST
♠ Q 10 6 3   ♠ K J 9
♡ 8 7 5 3   ♡ 6 4 2
◇ 8 6 3   ◇ K 10 9
♣ 10 7   ♣ K J 9 6

SOUTH-D
♠ A 5
♡ K Q J
◇ A Q J 4
♣ A Q 3 2

Defense Tricks:

☐ ☐ ☐ ☐ ☐ ☐ ☐ ☐ ☐ ☐ ☐ ☐

Bid the hand your way:

North	East	South	West
_____	_____	_____	_____
_____	_____	_____	_____
_____	_____	_____	_____
_____	_____	_____	_____

Opening Lead _____

How the hand was bid:

SOUTH	WEST	NORTH	EAST
2 NT	Pass	3 NT	All Pass

Opening lead — ♠ 3

How the hand was played: Not suspecting his good fortune, South won the first trick with the ace of spades and thought to himself how nice it would be if the diamond finesse worked. So he led a heart to dummy's ace and returned a diamond to finesse with the queen.

The finesse worked, and South glowed with happiness. He cashed the ace of diamonds and then thought how nice it would be if the suit broke 3-3. So he led a low diamond and got his wish when both opponents followed suit.

The messenger of the gods waited by with a cynical smile on his face. He knew that no bridge player is every satisfied, even if he gets exactly what he asks for.

TAKE SPADES

The defenders took their spades, thus amassing four tricks. Then West got out safely with a heart and waited for South to lead clubs from his own hand. East got the setting trick with the king of clubs.

South's trouble was that he had asked for the wrong finesse. It was possible to get three diamond tricks without a finesse; but he needed a club finesse for two tricks in that suit.

After taking the ace of spades, South should lead out the ace and then the queen of diamonds. He gets three diamond tricks with the 3-3 break in the suit. Later, South leads a heart to dummy's ace and tries the club finesse. He gets three diamonds, two clubs, one spade and three hearts for a total of nine tricks.

South is still complaining about his luck, but nobody listens anymore.

Manage Entries for Trump Coup

It's never pleasant to discover that the trumps are breaking badly, but you can protect yourself against disaster if you arrange
to make the discovery at the right time. This may require you to
play a suit backwards.

North dealer   **Both sides vulnerable**

NORTH-D
♠ K 7 6
♡ A 7
◇ 10 7 5
♣ A Q 8 4 2

WEST   EAST
♠ J 9 5 2   ♠ Q 10
♡ 6   ♡ J 8 5 4
◇ A K 8 6 2   ◇ Q J 9
♣ 7 6 5   ♣ K 10 9 3

SOUTH
♠ A 8 4 3
♡ K Q 10 9 3 2
◇ 4 3
♣ J

Defense Tricks:

☐ ☐ ☐ ☐ ☐ ☐ ☐ ☐ ☐ ☐ ☐ ☐

Bid the hand your way:

North	East	South	West
_____	_____	_____	_____
_____	_____	_____	_____
_____	_____	_____	_____
_____	_____	_____	_____
		Opening Lead	_____

How the hand was bid:

NORTH	EAST	SOUTH	WEST
1 ♣	Pass	1 ♡	Pass
1 NT	Pass	3 ♡	Pass
4 ♡	All Pass		

Opening lead — ◊ K

How the hand was played: South ruffed the third diamond and led the jack of clubs around to East's king. Back came a club to dummy's queen, and South discarded a spade.

South needed only a normal trump break for his contract. He cashed the ace and king of hearts, discovering the bad break. Then he could get back to dummy only once—not enough to make the contract.

The correct play is to play the hearts backwards. That is, South should win the first trump in his hand with the king and the next in dummy with the ace.

South discovers the bad trump break while he is in dummy rather than in his own hand. There is still time to execute a trump coup.

RUFFS CLUB

Declarer discards a spade on the ace of clubs and ruffs a club. Now he leads a spade to the king and leads the eight of clubs from dummy.

East discards a spade, since a ruff would be fatal. South throws the ace of spades and leads again from the dummy. East's trumps are caught in the middle, and South makes his game.

It goes against the grain to play the hearts in such a way as to block the suit at the second trick. If the trumps happened to break, however, South could get to his hand with the ace of spades to draw the last trump. When the trumps fail to break, South can get one additional ruff and still return to dummy to pick up the trumps without loss.

Advance Planning Puts You in Hand

When you were in the cradle, your parents probably asked you the old riddle: Why does a chicken cross the street? Bridge players know another riddle: Why does a chicken avoid crossing the street?

North dealer   **Both sides vulnerable**

NORTH-D
♠ A Q 9 8
♡ A 10 5 2
◇ A Q 7 5 4
♣ None

WEST	EAST
♠ 5 4 2	♠ None
♡ K Q 6	♡ J 9 8 4 3
◇ 10 8 2	◇ K J 9 3
♣ A Q 7 2	♣ 10 6 5 3

SOUTH
♠ K J 10 7 6 3
♡ 7
◇ 6
♣ K J 9 8 4

Defense Tricks:

☐ ☐ ☐ ☐ ☐ ☐ ☐ ☐ ☐ ☐ ☐ ☐ ☐

Bid the hand your way:

North	East	South	West
_____	_____	_____	_____
_____	_____	_____	_____
_____	_____	_____	_____
_____	_____	_____	_____

Opening Lead _____

30

How the hand was bid:

NORTH	EAST	SOUTH	WEST
1 ♦	Pass	1 ♠	Pass
2 ♡	Pass	2 ♠	Pass
4 ♠	Pass	6 ♠	All Pass

Opening lead — ♠ 2

How the hand was played: The trump opening lead prevented South from winning ten trump tricks by a crossruff. He had to plan to make twelve tricks by setting up dummy's queen of diamonds in addition to ruffing three clubs in dummy and eventually drawing trumps.

There's nothing difficult about any single play; South must simply have as much sense as a chicken. The actual declarer didn't know which side of the street he wanted to be on.

South made his mistake at the first trick when he allowed dummy's eight of spades to hold. He took the ace of diamonds, ruffed a diamond, ruffed a club in dummy, ruffed a second diamond, a second club, a third diamond and a third club.

STUCK IN DUMMY

But now South was stuck in dummy. He couldn't cash the queen of diamonds because West would ruff. The only other play was to cash the ace of hearts and ruff a heart, but then he would never get back to dummy for the queen of diamonds.

Any good chicken would overtake the first trick with the ten of spades. Then South ruffs a club, cashes the ace of diamonds, ruffs a diamond, ruffs a second club, a second diamond, a third club and a third diamond.

Now South has done all his work and he is in his own hand, exactly where he wants to be. He can draw the last two trumps and lead a heart to dummy's ace so that he can cash the queen of diamonds.

Courageous Play May Not Be Wise

You sometimes see people carry on with business as usual even though their houses and shops are burning around them. This is very courageous, but not very sensible. The same distinction exists in certain bridge hands.

North dealer   **East-West vulnerable**

NORTH-D
♠ Q 8 6
♡ A Q J 5
◇ Q
♣ A Q 9 4 2

WEST	EAST
♠ K 4 3	♠ A
♡ 9 3	♡ 8 7 4 2
◇ 10 8 7 5 3	◇ A 9 4 2
♣ 10 8 3	♣ K J 7 6

SOUTH
♠ J 10 9 7 5 2
♡ K 10 6
◇ K J 6
♣ 5

Defense Tricks:

☐ ☐ ☐ ☐ ☐ ☐ ☐ ☐ ☐ ☐ ☐ ☐ ☐ ☐

Bid the hand your way:

North	East	South	West
——	——	——	——
——	——	——	——
——	——	——	——
——	——	——	——
		Opening Lead	——

How the hand was bid:

NORTH	EAST	SOUTH	WEST
1 ♣	Pass	1 ♠	Pass
2 ♡	Pass	2 ♠	Pass
3 ♠	Pass	4 ♠	All Pass
			Opening lead — ♡ 9

How the hand was played: Declarer won the first trick in dummy with the jack of hearts and courageously led the six of spades from dummy. The hand was about to blow up in his face, but South wasn't going to show the white feather.

East took the ace of spades and led another heart. Declarer led another trump to West's king, and back came a diamond to East's ace.

Now East led a third heart, and West's ruff defeated the contract. During all this time, South never winced or showed any displeasure or pain. Very admirable.

IF YOU INSIST

Not so admirable if you insist on making a cold contract when you can.

After all, it isn't too hard for South to see the danger of a heart ruff. Why should he draw trumps as usual when this will give the opponents time to get their ruff?

Declarer should lead dummy's queen of diamonds instead of a trump at the second trick. He wins the heart return and cashes the king and jack of diamonds to discard two hearts from the dummy.

That takes all the hearts out of the dummy and guarantees the contract since dummy cannot be overruffed except by the ace or king of spades.

Not All Finesses Will Do You Good

There's nothing most of us like better than a chance to get something for nothing, and at the bridge table this usually means a finesse. Still, not all finesses are equally useful even though they may look equally enticing.

North dealer   **Neither side vulnerable**

NORTH-D
- ♠ K 6 2
- ♡ A Q 5 4
- ◇ A 4 3
- ♣ K 8 6

WEST
- ♠ J 10 9 3
- ♡ 8
- ◇ K 8 7 5
- ♣ 9 7 4 3

EAST
- ♠ Q 8 7 5 4
- ♡ K 2
- ◇ 10 9 6
- ♣ Q 5 2

SOUTH
- ♠ A
- ♡ J 10 9 7 6 3
- ◇ Q J 2
- ♣ A J 10

Defense Tricks:

☐ ☐ ☐ ☐ ☐ ☐ ☐ ☐ ☐ ☐ ☐ ☐ ☐

Bid the hand your way:

North	East	South	West
___	___	___	___
___	___	___	___
___	___	___	___
		Opening Lead ___	

34

How the hand was bid:

NORTH	EAST	SOUTH	WEST
1 NT	Pass	3 ♡	Pass
4 ◊	Pass	6 ♡	All Pass
			Opening lead — ♠ J

How the hand was played: South won the first trick with the ace of spades and immediately tried the heart finesse. East took the king of hearts and returned a spade to dummy's king.

South got rid of a diamond on the second spade trick, drew another trump and finessed successfully through the king of diamonds. But then the slam still depended on a finesse in clubs, and South happened to guess the wrong way to finesse.

"Bad luck," you may say. Or perhaps, "Bad guessing." It was neither; it was actually bad management.

NEEDED DIAMOND FINESSE

South needed the diamond finesse to make his slam, but he didn't need the heart finesse and he didn't have to guess the right way to finesse in clubs.

After winning the first trick with the ace of spades, South should immediately lead the jack of diamonds to find out whether or not that finesse will work.

When the diamond holds, South leads the low diamond to dummy's ace, cashes the king of spades to get rid of the queen of diamonds, ruffs a spade, leads a trump to dummy's ace and ruffs dummy's last diamond.

This eliminates spades and diamonds from the North and South hands. Declarer then gives up a trick to the king of hearts and waits for the return with his pencil poised to score the slam. If East returns a club, declarer gets a free finesse; if East returns anything else, dummy ruffs while South discards a club.

Experts Beat Elephants

One of the charming things about bridge experts is that they have such long memories. One member of a well-known team flubbed a hand in an important match recently, and it will probably be ten years before his teammates (and opponents) let him forget about it.

North dealer   **Both sides vulnerable**

NORTH-D

♠ A 8 7 6 2
♡ A Q 8
♢ A K 10 7 3
♣ None

WEST	EAST
♠ None	♠ K J 10 9 5 3
♡ 9 7 4 3	♡ None
♢ J 8 4	♢ Q 9 5 2
♣ A K 8 7 4 3	♣ J 9 5

SOUTH

♠ Q 4
♡ K J 10 6 5 2
♢ 6
♣ Q 10 6 2

Defense Tricks:

☐ ☐ ☐ ☐ ☐ ☐ ☐ ☐ ☐ ☐ ☐ ☐ ☐ ☐ ☐

Bid the hand your way:

North	East	South	West
_____	_____	_____	_____
_____	_____	_____	_____
_____	_____	_____	_____
_____	_____	_____	_____
		Opening Lead _____	

How the hand was bid:

NORTH	EAST	SOUTH	WEST
1 ♠	Pass	2 ♡	Pass
3 ◇	Pass	3 ♡	Pass
6 ♡	All Pass		

Opening lead — ♣ K

How the hand was played: West opened the king of clubs, and our expert friend ruffed in dummy. He thought he could make the slam if East had the king of spades, and perhaps even if not, so he led a small spade from dummy.

It was not a good idea. East stepped up with the king of spades, and West thoughtfully discarded a diamond to make it quite clear that he wasn't following suit. East led another spade, of course, and West ruffed to defeat the slam.

"There must have been another way to play it," North remarked with some bitterness.

"He'd have made it if I hadn't led a spade right back," East pointed out helpfully. Nobody thanked him for this comment.

OTHER WAY

There was another way to play the hand, depending only on a 4-3 break of the missing diamonds. The odds favor this by almost 2 to 1.

After ruffing the first club in dummy, declarer should cash the ace of trumps and the ace of diamonds. He ruffs a diamond in his hand, ruffs another club in dummy and ruffs another diamond in his hand.

Now South can draw three more rounds of trumps, discarding low spades from the dummy. He can then lead a spade to dummy to cash the king of diamonds and the last diamond, fulfilling the slam.

Expert Avoids Getting Stranded

You probably read recently about the teachers who tried to travel to Europe and got stranded in New York. If they had been expert travelers, as bridge tournament stars usually are, they would have known how to get back and forth.

South dealer   **Both sides vulnerable**

```
                    NORTH
                    ♠ K Q 10 4
                    ♡ A K 6 5 2
                    ◊ 6
                    ♣ A 10 3

        WEST                        EAST
        ♠ A 6 3 2                   ♠ 5
        ♡ Q J 8 3                   ♡ 10 9 7
        ◊ J 8 4                     ◊ Q 10 9 5
        ♣ 7 5                       ♣ 9 8 6 4 2

                    SOUTH-D
                    ♠ J 9 8 7
                    ♡ 4
                    ◊ A K 7 3 2
                    ♣ K Q J
```

Defense Tricks:

☐ ☐ ☐ ☐ ☐ ☐ ☐ ☐ ☐ ☐ ☐ ☐ ☐

Bid the hand your way:

North	East	South	West
_____	_____	_____	_____
_____	_____	_____	_____
_____	_____	_____	_____
_____	_____	_____	_____
		Opening Lead _____	

How the hand was bid:

SOUTH	WEST	NORTH	EAST
1 ◇	Pass	1 ♡	Pass
1 ♠	Pass	3 ♣	Pass
3 ◇	Pass	4 NT	Pass
5 ◇	Pass	6 ♠	All Pass

Opening lead — ♠ A

How the hand was played: Test your traveling skill on this hand, played in a national tournament by Don Krauss, noted young Los Angeles expert. You have to decide where home is and then make sure you can get back to it.

West opens the ace of spades and continues with a low spade. Do you plan to ruff hearts in your own hand or diamonds in the dummy?

HEART FAILURE

The plan to ruff hearts in your own hand will fail because you will get stranded away from home. Suppose you cash the ace of hearts, ruff a heart, lead a club to dummy's ace and ruff another heart.

You are now in the South hand, with no way to get back to dummy. You cannot draw the rest of West's trumps, and you can't make the slam while West has his trumps.

Try a different plan. After winning the second trick with a spade in either hand, you cash the ace of diamonds and ruff a diamond in dummy. Get to your hand with the king of clubs and ruff another diamond in dummy. Get to your hand again with the queen of clubs and draw West's remaining trumps.

Now you are home, where you want to be. You have the rest of the tricks because you saw that the clubs gave you an extra ticket to the South hand.

The moral of the bridge hand is quite clear; Count your entries before you decide which hand is home base.

Sporting Play Loses Contract

Ivar Stakgold, professor of mathematics at Northwestern University, is one of the best bridge players in the United States. As you might imagine, he has the pleasure of answering hundreds of questions on bridge mathematics.

South dealer   **Both sides vulnerable**

```
                    NORTH
                ♠ Q J 10 8
                ♡ Q 7 5 4 3
                ◇ 6
                ♣ 10 4 2

      WEST                    EAST
   ♠ 5 2                    ♠ 4 3
   ♡ 9 8                    ♡ K J 10 6 2
   ◇ A Q 10 7 5             ◇ J 9 8
   ♣ K J 6 3               ♣ Q 8 7

                    SOUTH-D
                ♠ A K 9 7 6
                ♡ A
                ◇ K 4 3 2
                ♣ A 9 5
```

Defense Tricks:

Bid the hand your way:

North	East	South	West
_____	_____	_____	_____
_____	_____	_____	_____
_____	_____	_____	_____
_____	_____	_____	_____

Opening Lead _____

How the hand was bid:

SOUTH	WEST	NORTH	EAST
1 ♠	Pass	2 ♠	Pass
4 ♠	All Pass		

Opening lead — ♡ 9

How the hand was played: Stakgold's partner, playing the South cards, won the first trick with the ace of hearts and led a spade to dummy in order to return the singleton diamond. When East failed to put up the ace, declarer shrewdly played low.

South's shrewdness didn't help him. East returned a trump, and South could ruff only two diamonds in dummy. He eventually lost a second diamond and two clubs.

"Bad luck," South complained. "Everything was wrong."

Stakgold smiled sympathetically. (He has had years of practice smiling at students who are about to fail.)

WONDERFUL CHANCE

"I had a wonderful chance," South remarked. "I would have made the contract if the ace of diamonds had been right for me, or if they didn't lead a trump back or if two ruffs dropped the ace of diamonds or the king of hearts. How much were the odds in my favor?"

"About 3 to 1," Stakgold replied. "The way you played the hand was very sporting."

Glowing with pride at this praise, South went on to the next hand and further deeds of derring-do. He didn't realize he was called "sporting" because he had given the opponents a chance to beat him when his contract was ice-cold.

After winning the first trick with the ace of hearts, South should lead a diamond from his hand. Even if the opponents returned a trump, South can still ruff three diamonds in the dummy, losing only one diamond and two clubs.

Save Your Key to Open Door

There's nothing like getting home from a vacation with your car keys and the keys to various hotel rooms but no key to your own house. Many bridge players practice this kind of foolishness and chalk the results up to bad luck.

South dealer   **North-South vulnerable**

NORTH
♠ K 9 6 2
♡ J 10
♢ J 10 9 2
♣ J 4 2

WEST   EAST
♠ Q J 10 8 5 4   ♠ 3
♡ K   ♡ 9 7 4 2
♢ K 8 5 4 3   ♢ A Q 7 6
♣ 7   ♣ 8 6 5 3

SOUTH-D
♠ A 7
♡ A Q 8 6 5 3
♢ None
♣ A K Q 10 9

Defense Tricks:

☐ ☐ ☐ ☐ ☐ ☐ ☐ ☐ ☐ ☐ ☐ ☐ ☐

Bid the hand your way:

North	East	South	West
_____	_____	_____	_____
_____	_____	_____	_____
_____	_____	_____	_____
_____	_____	_____	_____
		Opening Lead	_____

How the hand was bid:

SOUTH	WEST	NORTH	EAST
1 ♡	3 ♠	Double	Pass
4 ♣	Pass	5 ♣	Pass
6 ♣	All Pass		

Opening lead — ♠ Q

How the hand was played: South won the first trick with the ace of spades, thus using up an entry to his hand for no good reason. He drew two rounds of trumps with the ace and king, pausing for thought when West showed out.

Declarer's next move was to lead a club to dummy's jack to try the heart finesse. West won with the king of hearts and returned a diamond to make declarer ruff.

BAD BREAK

South drew the last trump and cashed the ace of hearts. Unfortunately, the hearts broke badly. The hand blew up, and South was down three.

Declarer can make his contract by working on the hearts before drawing trumps, but this is dangerous. Conceivably, he may lose a heart trick and a heart ruff (if West has four hearts to the king instead of a singleton king).

The simplest way to protect the slam is to win the first trick in dummy with the king of spades. South next draws four rounds of trumps and leads a low heart. If the opponent who takes the king of hearts returns a diamond to force out South's last trump, South can lead a heart to dummy's jack and get back with the ace of spades to cash the rest of the hearts.

In a manner of speaking, the ace of spades is the key to the South hand. South must save the key instead of throwing it away at the first trick.

Control the Trumps to Control the Play

In many hands, the key to success is to draw exactly two rounds of trumps before going on with your other plans. If you're violent with the key, however, it may break before you manage to open the door.

North dealer   **Both sides vulnerable**

NORTH-D
♠ 9 5
♡ 10 6 4 2
♢ A K 9 8
♣ K Q 10

WEST	EAST
♠ Q 10 7 3	♠ K J 6
♡ 9 8	♡ K Q J
♢ 10 5 2	♢ Q J 6 3
♣ 9 7 6 2	♣ 8 5 4

SOUTH
♠ A 8 4 2
♡ A 7 5 3
♢ 7 4
♣ A J 3

Defense Tricks:

☐ ☐ ☐ ☐ ☐ ☐ ☐ ☐ ☐ ☐ ☐ ☐

Bid the hand your way:

North	East	South	West
_____	_____	_____	_____
_____	_____	_____	_____
_____	_____	_____	_____
_____	_____	_____	_____
		Opening Lead	_____

How the hand was bid:

NORTH	EAST	SOUTH	WEST
1 ◊	Pass	1 ♡	Pass
2 ♡	Pass	3 NT	Pass
4 ♡	All Pass		

Opening lead — ♠ 3

How the hand was played: South refused the first spade trick, shrewdly enough, but took the second trick with the ace of spades. After this promising start, South went full speed ahead with the trumps, leading out the ace and then a low trump.

East won the second round of trumps and promptly drew a third trump, thus leaving only one trump in the dummy. South could ruff only one of his two losing spades and eventually had to give up the other spade for a loss of 100 points.

North was vaguely dissatisfied. "If you study the hand hard enough," he suggested, "you can probably find a way to go down two."

SHOULD MAKE CONTRACT

South can make the contract by drawing only two rounds of trumps. He wants to leave two trumps in dummy to take care of the two losing spades but he doesn't want to risk an overruff of dummy by a player who started with only two trumps.

After taking the second trick with the ace of spades, South should lead a low trump. No matter what is returned, South can draw exactly one more round of trumps with the ace—and then he abandons trumps.

South ruffs a spade in dummy, gets to his hand with a club and ruffs his last spade. The defenders get, in all, two trumps and the first spade—and South is spared his partner's sarcasm.

Choose Right Suit for Double Chance

When you must develop one additional trick in either of two suits, you may not have to choose one suit or the other. Start the right suit and you may then be able to fall back on the other suit if your first attempt fails.

South dealer   Both sides vulnerable

                              NORTH
                              ♠ Q 4
                              ♡ A 5
                              ◇ J 9 5 4
                              ♣ K Q 9 7 5

              WEST   EAST
              ♠ A J 7 6 2   ♠ 10 9 3
              ♡ 9 6 2   ♡ J 10 8 3
              ◇ 7 6 2   ◇ K Q
              ♣ 10 3   ♣ J 6 4 2

                              SOUTH-D
                              ♠ K 8 5
                              ♡ K Q 7 4
                              ◇ A 10 8 3
                              ♣ A 8

Defense Tricks:

☐ ☐ ☐ ☐ ☐ ☐ ☐ ☐ ☐ ☐ ☐ ☐ ☐

Bid the hand your way:

North	East	South	West
___	___	___	___
___	___	___	___
___	___	___	___
___	___	___	___

Opening Lead _____

How the hand was bid:

SOUTH	WEST	NORTH	EAST
1 NT	Pass	3 NT	All Pass

Opening lead — ♠ 6

How the hand was played: Dummy's queen of spades held the first trick, and South could count seven other fast tricks. He needed one other trick for his contract, obviously in diamonds or clubs.

South tried diamonds first. He led a low diamond from dummy, and East put up the queen with such alacrity that South wisely took the ace and abandoned the suit. He dared not let East in with the king of diamonds to return a spade.

South next tried the clubs, but he had to lead out the three top clubs. When the jack failed to drop, the jig was up. South cashed his top hearts and led a fourth heart in the hope that West would get in, but there was no such luck. East took his tricks and led a spade, defeating the contract.

SHOULD PLAY CLUBS

At the second trick, declarer should lead a low club from dummy. When East plays low, South passes the trick to West by playing the eight. No matter what West returns, declarer can cash the ace of clubs and get to dummy with the ace of hearts to run the rest of the clubs.

The play for clubs fails if East can put up the jack or ten of clubs on the first round of the suit. If so, South cashes three top clubs to see if the suit will break. If this fails, there is still time to lead a diamond from dummy in the hope of finding at least one high diamond in the West hand.

Half a loaf may be better than none, but the whole loaf is best of all.

Don't Give Up Game without Struggle

When you've won several rubbers in a row, your opponents tend to be depressed. Keep playing and make the most of your psychological advantage. When you've lost several rubbers in a row, you may be the depressed one. Stop playing as soon as you conveniently can.

North dealer   **North-South vulnerable**

NORTH-D

♠ K Q
♡ Q 4 2
♢ A K J
♣ K Q 10 7 6

WEST	EAST
♠ 10 9 7 5 4	♠ A 6 3 2
♡ K 3	♡ 9 8 5
♢ 10 6 4	♢ 9 8 7 5
♣ A 9 2	♣ 5 3

SOUTH

♠ J 8
♡ A J 10 7 6
♢ Q 3 2
♣ J 8 4

Defense Tricks:

☐ ☐ ☐ ☐ ☐ ☐ ☐ ☐ ☐ ☐ ☐ ☐ ☐

Bid the hand your way:

North	East	South	West
_____	_____	_____	_____
_____	_____	_____	_____
_____	_____	_____	_____
_____	_____	_____	_____

Opening Lead _____

How the hand was bid:

NORTH	EAST	SOUTH	WEST
1 ♣	Pass	1 ♡	Pass
2 NT	Pass	3 ♡	Pass
4 ♡	All Pass		

Opening lead — ♠ 5

How the hand was played: East had lost five rubbers in a row before playing this hand and was sure that nothing good could possibly happen. He won the first trick with the ace of spades and despairingly returned a spade to dummy's king.

Declarer had no problems. He lost the trump finesse but then had an easy time drawing the rest of the trumps. He gave up one club trick, and East had another rubber to moan about.

East can defeat the contract if he is alert instead of depressed. A glance at the dummy makes it clear that his side can get only one spade trick and no diamond trick. Three additional tricks are needed to defeat the contact, and they must be found in hearts and clubs.

OPTIMISM REQUIRED

East should reason that West may have a high heart and the ace of clubs or conceivably the A-K of hearts without a high club. West cannot have all three of the missing high cards in view of South's bidding. Since two tricks will not defeat the contract, East must try for a club ruff.

In short, East must optimistically return a club at the second trick. West takes the ace of clubs and returns the suit, hoping that East can ruff at once.

Declarer tries to draw trumps quickly by taking the ace of hearts and returning a trump, but West steps up with the king of hearts and returns a third club for East to ruff. The ruff defeats the contract.

Look at Rhinoceros to Finesse

It must have been a bridge player who stared incredulously at a rhinoceros and declared: "There's no such animal." The same unwillingness to look a fact in the eye caused South's downfall in this hand.

West dealer   **East-West vulnerable**

                          NORTH
                          ♠ J 9 5
                          ♡ A 10 4
                          ◇ Q J 8 7
                          ♣ 10 8 4

        WEST-D   EAST
        ♠ A K 10 8 6   ♠ Q 7 3
        ♡ 8 3   ♡ 7 6 2
        ◇ K 10 9 4   ◇ 6 5 2
        ♣ Q 5   ♣ J 9 6 3

                          SOUTH
                          ♠ 4 2
                          ♡ K Q J 9 5
                          ◇ A 3
                          ♣ A K 7 2

Defense Tricks:

☐ ☐ ☐ ☐ ☐ ☐ ☐ ☐ ☐ ☐ ☐ ☐ ☐

Bid the hand your way:

North	East	South	West
_____	_____	_____	_____
_____	_____	_____	_____
_____	_____	_____	_____
_____	_____	_____	_____
		Opening Lead _____	

50

How the hand was bid:

WEST	NORTH	EAST	SOUTH
1 ♠	Pass	Pass	Double
Pass	2 ◇	Pass	2 ♡
Pass	3 ♡	Pass	4 ♡
All Pass			

Opening lead — ♠ K

How the hand was played: West took two top spades and led a third spade to make South ruff. Declarer led a trump to dummy's ten and returned the queen of diamonds, losing to the king.

West got out safely with a trump, and South eventually discarded one club on the jack of diamonds. He still had to give up a club. Down one.

The rhinoceros in the ointment was the king of diamonds. All the evidence made it clear that the king was nestling securely in West's hand.

To begin with, West needed the king of diamonds for his vulnerable opening bid. For another, East would have spoken at his first or second turn if he had the king of diamonds in addition to his Q-x-x of spades.

SHOULD MAKE CONTRACT

South should make the contract by facing the fact that West has the king of diamonds. After ruffing the third spade, South simply leads his low diamond.

If West takes his king, South can later clear the ace of diamonds out of the way and draw three rounds of trumps ending in the dummy. Then he discards both low clubs on the queen and jack of diamonds.

If West fails to take the king of diamonds, South gets no discards but doesn't lose a diamond trick. He can take the top clubs, give up a club and ruff his last club in dummy. Either way the contract is home.

Save Your Brains for Second Trap

If you avoid the first pitfall of a bridge hand, don't swoon with delight and surprise. You may need all of your brains and alertness to avoid the next trap. Some bridge hands are nasty enough to put you to the test a second time.

South dealer   Both sides vulnerable

NORTH

♠ K Q 5 2
♡ 8 7 2
♢ A K 6 5
♣ 8 4

WEST   EAST

♠ 9 8 7 3   ♠ A 10 6
♡ Q 4 3   ♡ 6 5
♢ J 10   ♢ Q 9 8 2
♣ K J 5 2   ♣ 10 9 6 3

SOUTH-D

♠ J 4
♡ A K J 10 9
♢ 7 4 3
♣ A Q 7

Defense Tricks:

□ □ □ □ □ □ □ □ □ □ □ □ □

Bid the hand your way:

North	East	South	West
———	———	———	———
———	———	———	———
———	———	———	———
———	———	———	———
		Opening Lead ———	

How the hand was bid:

SOUTH	WEST	NORTH	EAST
1 ♡	Pass	1 ♠	Pass
2 ♡	Pass	4 ♡	All Pass

Opening lead — ◇ J

How the hand was played: Declarer took the first diamond in dummy with the king and shrewdly avoided the temptation of trying a trump finesse. He would lose to the queen of trumps, back would come a diamond and then he would lose a trick in each suit.

Instead, South led a spade from dummy at the second trick. The jack won, and South led another spade to drive out the ace with dummy's queen. Now if East returned a diamond to the ace, dummy could lead the king of spades to let South get rid of his last diamond.

South was so proud of playing the right suit first that he didn't see the danger when East returned a trump. South tried a finesse, losing to the queen.

STOPS RUFF

West returned a trump to the nine. South led to the ace of diamonds, discarded his last diamond on the king of spades and then tried the club finesse.

West took the king of clubs and took the last trump out of dummy. Now South had to lose a second club trick—which cost him the game and rubber.

South should make the contract by refusing to try an early trump finesse. Declarer should win the first trump with the ace, make his diamond and spade plays and then try the club finesse with two trumps still in the dummy.

The club finesse loses, but West cannot get the trumps out of dummy. South can take the ace of clubs and ruff a club; only then is it safe for him to try the trump finesse.

Players Resist Valuing Tens

Scientists have discovered that even the cleverest penguins won't buy electric fans. And most bridge players won't buy the idea that a stray ten is often worth a full trick. Neither birds nor people will buy what they don't know how to use.

South dealer   **Both sides vulnerable**

NORTH
- ♠ Q J 9 5 4
- ♡ A J 5
- ◊ J 4
- ♣ K 10 2

WEST
- ♠ 10 6
- ♡ 9 7 6
- ◊ Q 10 9 8
- ♣ J 8 7 6

EAST
- ♠ 7
- ♡ Q 10 8 3
- ◊ K 7 6 2
- ♣ A Q 9 5

SOUTH-D
- ♠ A K 8 3 2
- ♡ K 4 2
- ◊ A 5 3
- ♣ 4 3

Defense Tricks:

☐ ☐ ☐ ☐ ☐ ☐ ☐ ☐ ☐ ☐ ☐ ☐ ☐

Bid the hand your way:

North	East	South	West
_____	_____	_____	_____
_____	_____	_____	_____
_____	_____	_____	_____
_____	_____	_____	_____
		Opening Lead _____	

How the hand was bid:

SOUTH	WEST	NORTH	EAST
1 ♠	Pass	3 ♠	Pass
4 ♠	All Pass		

Opening lead — ◇ 10

How the hand was played: South won the first trick with the ace of diamonds, drew trumps and led a club to dummy's king. East won with the ace, continued with the queen of clubs and led a third club to make South ruff.

Declarer next tried the heart finesse, losing to the queen. The defenders then took a diamond trick, defeating the contract.

South lost his contract because he didn't see the value of dummy's ten of clubs. After the opening lead, South could make his contract against any defense.

REFUSE FIRST TRICK

South should begin by playing the jack of diamonds from dummy. East puts up the king, and South must refuse the first trick. The idea is to make sure that West can never regain the lead with a diamond.

East returns a diamond at the second trick, and South takes the ace. Declarer ruffs a diamond in dummy, draws two rounds of trumps and then leads a low club.

If West plays low, declarer plays dummy's ten of clubs. East must win with the queen of clubs. If East then returns a club, dummy's king will take a trick. If East, instead, returns a heart, dummy gets a free finesse. And if East returns a diamond, dummy ruffs while South discards a losing club or heart.

West cannot save his partner by putting up the jack of clubs when South leads the club. Declarer can then play dummy's king. East wins with the ace, but dummy's ten will become good if East continues clubs.

Fishermen Usually Find Fish

The best bait in the world won't work when there are no fish in the stream. Fortunately, for those of us who do our angling at the bridge table, there's no end to the supply of poor fish.

South dealer   **East-West vulnerable**

NORTH

♠ K Q 4 2
♡ K 7 5
◇ K Q 4
♣ 9 7 4

WEST

♠ 8 7
♡ 9 4 2
◇ 9 8 7 6
♣ K J 8 2

EAST

♠ A J 9 6
♡ Q J 10 8 3
◇ 5 2
♣ Q 6

SOUTH-D

♠ 10 5 3
♡ A 6
◇ A J 10 3
♣ A 10 5 3

Defense Tricks:

☐ ☐ ☐ ☐ ☐ ☐ ☐ ☐ ☐ ☐ ☐ ☐ ☐

Bid the hand your way:

North	East	South	West
_____	_____	_____	_____
_____	_____	_____	_____
_____	_____	_____	_____
_____	_____	_____	_____

Opening Lead _____

How the hand was bid:

SOUTH	WEST	NORTH	EAST
1 ◊	Pass	1 ♠	Pass
1 NT	Pass	3 NT	All Pass

Opening lead — ◊ 9

How the hand was played: West couldn't think of a good attacking lead so hit upon the passive lead of the nine of diamonds. A heart would have been better, as it turned out, but West couldn't tell.

South could count on four diamonds, two hearts, one club and at least one spade. He correctly decided that his best chance was to try for two spade tricks instead of only one. With this in mind, South won the first diamond in his hand and led a spade to dummy's king.

West naturally played a low spade, and East played the six of spades so smoothly that South was completely taken in. South was convinced that West had the ace of spades.

SWALLOWS BAIT

South ran his diamonds and swallowed the bait by leading another spade to dummy's queen. East could now haul in his fish by taking three spade tricks. These were not enough to defeat the contract immediately, but South had no further play for his ninth trick.

South's play to the second trick was correct, but when the king of spades won he should immediately return a low spade from dummy toward his own ten.

This guarantees two spade tricks whenever East has the jack of spades. If West has the jack of spades, declarer can get a second spade trick if West has the ace of spades since he can later lead his low spade toward dummy's queen. Any play will work if the six missing spades break 3-3.

The correct play would be easier to see if East took the first spade trick with the ace. The play is still correct even when East is sly enough to refuse the first spade.

Research Reveals Truth about Race

More than two thousand years ago the daily newspapers were full of the big race. Patient research reveals that the race was actually a bridge match between Diogenes Q. Hare and Aesop D. Tortoise and that Tortoise won in a walk when they both played the hand shown below.

North dealer   **Both sides vulnerable**

NORTH-D
♠ Q 10 8 3
♡ A K 6
◇ A K 7
♣ 9 6 2

WEST	EAST
♠ 6 4	♠ K J 9 2
♡ 8 7 5 2	♡ 4 3
◇ 6 5	◇ 9 4 3
♣ K Q J 10 7	♣ A 8 4 3

SOUTH
♠ A 7 5
♡ Q J 10 9
◇ Q J 10 8 2
♣ 5

Defense Tricks:

☐ ☐ ☐ ☐ ☐ ☐ ☐ ☐ ☐ ☐ ☐ ☐ ☐

Bid the hand your way:

North	East	South	West
————	————	————	————
————	————	————	————
————	————	————	————
————	————	————	————

Opening Lead ————

58

How the hand was bid:

NORTH	EAST	SOUTH	WEST
1 NT	Pass	2 ♣	Double
2 ♠	Pass	3 ◊	Pass
4 ◊	Pass	4 ♡	All Pass
			Opening lead — ♣ K

How the hand was played: At both tables of the match, West opened the king of clubs and continued the suit.

Hare ruffed the second club, thus taking over the lead. He drew three rounds of trumps, and that dull noise you may have heard two thousand years ago was Hare's jaw dropping when the trumps failed to break.

Hare turned to the diamonds, but couldn't get far with them. West ruffed the third diamond and ran the rest of his clubs. Down two.

SLOWER START

Tortoise was slower getting started. Instead of ruffing the second club he discarded a spade, allowing West to hold the trick. When West led a third club, Tortoise discarded his other low spade.

For lack of anything better to do, West led a fourth club. Tortoise ruffed in dummy with the ace of trumps just to show that he could be flashy when it pleased him. Then he drew four rounds of trumps.

Tortoise slowly took the rest of the tricks with the ace of spades and good diamonds, making his contract and winning the match. It took him fifteen minutes to make his contract, while Hare had managed to go down two in only five minutes.

The moral is clear: Now that you have been taught to discard losers rather than weaken your trump suit, you can play such hands with the speed of Hare and the accuracy of Tortoise.

Never Underestimate Power of Nine

"Take care of the nines and eights," says Poor Alfred's Almanac, "and the aces and kings will take care of themselves." Perhaps the saying was based on the hand shown below.

West dealer   **North-South vulnerable**

NORTH
♠ K Q 10 5
♡ A 9 7 6
◇ 9 4
♣ 8 4 3

WEST-D   **EAST**
♠ 6 3   ♠ A J 8 7 4 2
♡ 4 3   ♡ 5 2
◇ 10 8 7 6 2   ◇ K Q J
♣ K Q 10 7   ♣ 9 5

SOUTH
♠ 9
♡ K Q J 10 8
◇ A 5 3
♣ A J 6 2

Defense Tricks:

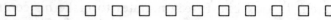

Bid the hand your way:

North	East	South	West
_____	_____	_____	_____
_____	_____	_____	_____
_____	_____	_____	_____
_____	_____	_____	_____
		Opening Lead _____	

How the hand was bid:

WEST	NORTH	EAST	SOUTH
Pass	Pass	1 ♠	2 ♡
Pass	3 ♡	Pass	4 ♡
All Pass			

Opening lead — ♠ 6

How the hand was played: West opened the six of spades and declarer lost his contract with his first play. He put up dummy's king of spades, losing to the ace.

East returned the king of diamonds to the ace, and declarer discarded a diamond on dummy's queen of spades after drawing trumps. This did South no good at all since he still had to lose a diamond and two clubs. Down one.

South went down because he didn't make good use of the nine of spades. He played the hand as though he had the singleton deuce of spades instead of the singleton nine.

MUST PLAY LOW

South should play the five of spades from dummy at the first trick. This permits East to win with the jack of spades, but East's triumph is short-lived

East returns the king of diamonds to the ace, whereupon South draws one round of trumps with the king and another by leading the eight to dummy's nine. He then returns the king of spades from dummy.

If East fails to put up the ace of spades promptly, South discards a diamond and continues with dummy's queen of spades. South is ready to ruff whenever East plays the ace of spades and to discard diamonds whenever East plays low.

Expert Looks Many Tricks Ahead

When you watch a good bridge player you see no surprises. He does everything you would do when you're playing well. The difference is he does it nearly all the time. Watching a great player is something else again. Then you see plays you wouldn't dream of making.

North dealer   **Both sides vulnerable**

NORTH-D
♠ 10 5 3
♡ A K 7 6 2
♢ 5 3 2
♣ A 6

WEST	EAST
♠ None	♠ J 9 8 2
♡ 10 5 4	♡ J 9 8 3
♢ J 8 7 6	♢ 4
♣ Q J 10 8 5 3	♣ K 9 4 2

SOUTH
♠ A K Q 7 6 4
♡ Q
♢ A K Q 10 9
♣ 7

Defense Tricks:

☐ ☐ ☐ ☐ ☐ ☐ ☐ ☐ ☐ ☐ ☐ ☐ ☐

Bid the hand your way:

North	East	South	West
_____	_____	_____	_____
_____	_____	_____	_____
_____	_____	_____	_____
_____	_____	_____	_____

Opening Lead _____

How the hand was bid:

NORTH	EAST	SOUTH	WEST
1 ♡	Pass	2 ♣	Pass
3 ♡	Pass	4 ◇	Pass
4 ♠	Pass	6 ♠	All Pass

Opening lead — ♣ Q

How the hand was played: When Harry Fishbein played this hand some years ago, he won the first trick in dummy with the ace of clubs. This play surprised nobody, but his next move astonished the kibitzers.

No, Fishbein did not lead a trump from dummy at the second trick. Instead, he led dummy's six of clubs and ruffed it in his hand. What good could this do?

Now Fishbein tackled the trumps. When South led the ace, West discarded a club, and the bad news was out.

ABANDONS TRUMPS

Fishbein abandoned trumps and led the queen of hearts. Then he began to cash high diamonds. He took the ace of diamonds and followed with the king.

What could East do? If he ruffed the king of diamonds and returned a heart, declarer would get to dummy to discard two diamonds on the top hearts. If East, instead, returned a trump, dummy's ten of spades would win a trick and South could discard diamonds on the top hearts.

East likewise could not afford to return a club, thanks to the play at the second trick. South would discard a diamond from his hand and ruff in dummy. Then he would cash a high heart to get rid of the other low diamond.

East decided not to ruff, so Fishbein continued with the queen of diamonds. When East discarded once more, Fishbein led a low diamond and ruffed in dummy. This set up the diamonds so that East could get the trump trick but there was no further danger for declarer.

Courage Needed to Give up Ace

We usually laugh at a player who loses an ace and accuse him of taking it to bed with him, but the play is sometimes correct. It may have been Sir Walter Scott who wrote the stirring lines: "Breathes there the man with soul so dead, who never has taken an ace to bed," and so on. Sir Walter had just witnessed the hand shown below.

West dealer   **North-South vulnerable**

```
                        NORTH
                        ♠ A 3 2
                        ♡ K Q J 10
                        ◇ 8 5 4
                        ♣ 6 4 3

        WEST-D                              EAST
        ♠ 7 5 4                             ♠ 6
        ♡ 2                                 ♡ A 9 8 7 5 4 3
        ◇ K 10 9 6 2                        ◇ Q J
        ♣ K 10 9 5                          ♣ Q J 8

                        SOUTH
                        ♠ K Q J 10 9 8
                        ♡ 6
                        ◇ A 7 3
                        ♣ A 7 2
```

Defense Tricks:

☐ ☐ ☐ ☐ ☐ ☐ ☐ ☐ ☐ ☐ ☐ ☐ ☐

Bid the hand your way:

North	East	South	West
_____	_____	_____	_____
_____	_____	_____	_____
_____	_____	_____	_____
_____	_____	_____	_____

Opening Lead _____

How the hand was bid:

WEST	NORTH	EAST	SOUTH
Pass	Pass	3 ♡	3 ♠
Pass	4 ♠	All Pass	

Opening lead — ♡ 2

How the hand was played: West opened the deuce of hearts, an obvious singleton, but East decided not to play his ace.

Declarer was somewhat surprised to win the first trick in dummy with the king of hearts but recovered in time to continue with the queen of hearts. East played low again.

South discarded a low diamond, and West ruffed. West returned a trump. South won with the king of spades and led a spade to dummy's ace.

Declarer then led another heart from dummy. This time East played his ace. South ruffed, and everybody laughed. Everybody, that is, except Sir Walter Scott.

LOSES FOUR TRICKS

South had already lost one trick to West's low trump, and South still had a losing diamond and two losing clubs. He eventually gave up these tricks and was down one.

The reason Sir Walter didn't laugh is that South could have made his contract if East had taken his ace of hearts at the first trick.

If East takes the ace of hearts and returns a heart, South discards a diamond. West ruffs, and the defense is off to a good start. West returns a diamond (as good a play as any), and South takes the ace.

South now draws trumps with the king and dummy's ace, after which he can safely cash dummy's two good hearts. He thus wins six trumps, two hearts and two side aces for a total of ten tricks. East's actual defense limited dummy to one heart trick, so that South won only nine tricks in all.

Let Brains Work Instead of Finesses

"Comes the Revolution, and all my finesses will work," my bearded friend threatened. "While you're waiting," I observed, "you'd be better off if you let your brains work instead of depending on the finesses."

South dealer   **Both sides vulnerable**

NORTH
♠ 7 6 5 3 2
♡ J 7 6 4
◇ A J
♣ A Q

WEST   EAST
♠ Q 10 8 4   ♠ K 9
♡ K Q 2   ♡ 3
◇ 8 4   ◇ Q 10 9 5 2
♣ J 7 6 3   ♣ K 10 9 5 2

SOUTH-D
♠ A J
♡ A 10 9 8 5
◇ K 7 6 3
♣ 8 4

Defense Tricks:

☐ ☐ ☐ ☐ ☐ ☐ ☐ ☐ ☐ ☐ ☐ ☐ ☐

Bid the hand your way:

North	East	South	West
_____	_____	_____	_____
_____	_____	_____	_____
_____	_____	_____	_____
_____	_____	_____	_____
		Opening Lead	_____

How the hand was bid:

SOUTH	WEST	NORTH	EAST
1 ♡	Pass	3 ♡	Pass
4 ♡	All Pass		

Opening lead — ♠ 4

How the hand was played: South won the first trick with the ace of spades and wondered whether to finesse with the jack of diamonds or the queen of clubs. After much useless thought, he tried the queen of clubs, losing to the king.

East returned a spade to the queen, and West eventually won two heart tricks. Down one.

"Four key cards, and they were all in the wrong position," South moaned. "I could take four finesses, but all four would lose. What have I done to deserve such luck?"

There was nothing wrong with South's luck—just with his line of play. South didn't need any finesses and should not have tried any.

SET UP SPADES

South should take the ace of spades and fire the jack of spades right back. When both opponents follow suit, South is home.

West returns a club, but declarer puts up dummy's ace. He ruffs a low spade, gets back to dummy with a diamond to ruff another low spade, cashes the ace of hearts, takes the king of diamonds and leads a low diamond.

If West ruffs, declarer throws the queen of clubs from dummy. If West fails to ruff, declarer ruffs the diamond in dummy and leads the last spade to discard the remaining club from his hand.

Either way, South avoids the loss of a club trick. He gives up only one spade and two trumps.

Take Any Reasonable Risk

"Is it necessary for a bridge player to be a mathematician?" asks a regular reader. "We had a big argument about a hand last night, but the conversation got too mathematical for us."

South dealer   **Both sides vulnerable**

NORTH
♠ K 8
♡ J 9 8
◇ J 6 2
♣ A 8 6 3 2

WEST   EAST
♠ Q 10 5 4   ♠ A J 7 6 2
♡ 10 3   ♡ 5
◇ Q 9 7   ◇ K 10 5 3
♣ K 10 7 4   ♣ Q J 5

SOUTH-D
♠ 9 3
♡ A K Q 7 6 4 2
◇ A 8 4
♣ 9

Defense Tricks:

☐ ☐ ☐ ☐ ☐ ☐ ☐ ☐ ☐ ☐ ☐ ☐

Bid the hand your way:

North	East	South	West
____	____	____	____
____	____	____	____
____	____	____	____
____	____	____	____

Opening Lead ____

How the hand was bid:

SOUTH	WEST	NORTH	EAST
1 ♡	Pass	2 ♡	Pass
4 ♡	All Pass		

Opening lead — ♠ 4

How the hand was played: "East took the first two spade tricks and returned a low diamond. South took the ace of diamonds and led out six rounds of trumps, but nobody made a helpful discard. Declarer finally went down one.

"Dummy said that South should set up the clubs. After winning with the ace of diamonds, he should take the ace of clubs, ruff a club and lead a low trump to finesse with dummy's eight. When this works, South can ruff a club, get back with a trump to ruff another club and get back with a trump to cash the last club.

"South said he would gain if West had the ten of hearts and if the clubs broke 4-3. If anything slipped, he would go down two instead of just one. In the long run, he said, it was better to settle for the smaller loss.

"Who is right?"

FINESSE IS EVEN SHOT

If South plays the hand ten times, he will lose the finesse five times and thus go down two. Three times out of ten he will make this contract. The other two times the finesse will work but the clubs will break badly.

Averaging out the ten hands, South scores plus 86 points per hand if he plays to make the contract. He scores minus 100 points per hand if he settles for down one. Who wants to give up 186 points per hand?

You don't have to work out your chances in this way. When you're not doubled, whether vulnerable or not, make any reasonable play that gives you a chance for your contract, even if failure will cost you an extra 100 points.

Players Operate on Budget

The choice between mink and cloth depends not only on which kind of coat you prefer but also on how much you have left after you have paid the grocer. The same principle applies in the play of some bridge hands.

North dealer   **Both sides vulnerable**

NORTH-D
♠ Q 8 7 3
♡ 10 9 6 3
◇ A Q
♣ Q J 10

WEST	EAST
♠ None	♠ K J 9
♡ 5 2	♡ K 8 7 4
◇ 10 9 8 6 5 2	◇ K J 4 3
♣ 9 7 6 3 2	♣ 8 4

SOUTH
♠ A 10 6 5 4 2
♡ A Q J
◇ 7
♣ A K 5

Defense Tricks:

☐ ☐ ☐ ☐ ☐ ☐ ☐ ☐ ☐ ☐ ☐ ☐ ☐

Bid the hand your way:

North	East	South	West
_____	_____	_____	_____
_____	_____	_____	_____
_____	_____	_____	_____
_____	_____	_____	_____

Opening Lead _____

70

How the hand was bid:

NORTH	EAST	SOUTH	WEST
Pass	Pass	1 ♠	Pass
3 ♠	Pass	6 ♠	All Pass
			Opening lead — ◊ 10

How the hand was played: Plan the play of the South hand without looking at the East-West cards. If you lead out the ace of spades, you may drop the king and win all thirteen tricks. But if you have bad luck, you may lose two trump tricks that way.

If you deliberately give up a spade trick to avoid the loss of two trumps, you may find out that you need all the trumps and that the king of spades is unguarded.

The solution to such problems does not depend solely on the spades. You must see what you can afford.

TRY HEARTS FIRST

Win the first diamond trick in dummy and try the heart finesse immediately. That is, lead a low heart from dummy and play the queen from your hand.

If the heart finesse loses, you must lead out the ace of spades and hope that a singleton king drops. If you lose a heart trick, you cannot afford to lose a trump trick.

If the heart finesse wins, you can afford to lose one trump trick. Just make sure you don't lose two trumps.

After winning the heart finesse, lead a low trump from your hand. If West follows suit with a low trump, you will play dummy's queen.

If West has no trumps, you play dummy's queen to force out the king. You ruff the diamond return, lead a club to dummy's queen and return a trump to finesse with the ten. Draw the last trump with the ace, lead a low trump to dummy's eight and then repeat the heart finesse.

Even Good Players May Be Careless

A good player has no business being careless, but the fact is that we all wander from the strait and narrow path. We think about something else and play a hand by instinct. Unfortunately, we are not born with an instinct for the proper play of slam contracts.

South dealer   **East-West vulnerable**

NORTH
♠ 7 5 3 2
♡ K 10 8 6
♢ 5 3
♣ K 6 4

WEST   EAST
♠ 10 8   ♠ A K Q J 9 6 4
♡ 5 3 2   ♡ None
♢ K 6 4 2   ♢ 10 9 8 7
♣ Q 10 9 7   ♣ 5 2

SOUTH-D
♠ None
♡ A Q J 9 7 4
♢ A Q J
♣ A J 8 3

Defense Tricks:

☐ ☐ ☐ ☐ ☐ ☐ ☐ ☐ ☐ ☐ ☐ ☐ ☐

Bid the hand your way:

North	East	South	West
_____	_____	_____	_____
_____	_____	_____	_____
_____	_____	_____	_____
_____	_____	_____	_____
		Opening Lead	_____

How the hand was bid:

SOUTH	WEST	NORTH	EAST
1 ♡	Pass	2 ♡	4 ♠
6 ♡	All Pass		

Opening lead — ♠ 10

How the hand was played: South beamed as he looked at the dummy. His jump to slam was going to pay off. It was a good, bold bid, and South felt proud of himself.

So proud, in fact, that he carelessly led the ace of hearts after ruffing the opening spade lead. The 3-0 trump break should have sobered declarer but he was still glowing with pride. He continued with a trump to dummy's eight.

Now the fat was in the fire. When declarer tried the diamond finesse, West won with the king of diamonds and returned his last trump. This left only one trump in the dummy; South eventually discovered that he could not ruff two clubs with only one trump.

South eventually lost a club trick. Down one at a cold slam contract.

SIMPLE PLAY

The correct play is simple. After ruffing the opening spade lead, South leads a trump to dummy. On discovering the bad trump break, declarer returns a diamond from dummy for the finesse.

West can win and return a trump, but that leaves two trumps in dummy. Declarer cashes the top diamonds to discard a club from dummy, takes the top clubs and the crossruffs clubs and spades.

South can recover from the careless play of the ace of hearts by leading a club to dummy's king instead of a second trump. Then he takes the diamond finesse. The important thing is to tackle the diamonds without giving West a chance to get three trumps out of the dummy.

Common Sense Is Rare Quality

The most interesting hands are those in which there is no need to make a weird or difficult play. You simply look ahead and use the most uncommon of all qualities: common sense.

South dealer   **North-South vulnerable**

NORTH
- ♠ A Q 7 6
- ♡ 9
- ◇ A 5 4
- ♣ A K 10 6 4

WEST
- ♠ 5 4 2
- ♡ Q 10 6 5 2
- ◇ K 7 6
- ♣ 9 2

EAST
- ♠ 3
- ♡ J 8 4
- ◇ J 10 9 8 3
- ♣ Q J 8 7

SOUTH-D
- ♠ K J 10 9 8
- ♡ A K 7 3
- ◇ Q 2
- ♣ 5 3

Defense Tricks:

☐ ☐ ☐ ☐ ☐ ☐ ☐ ☐ ☐ ☐ ☐ ☐

Bid the hand your way:

North	East	South	West
_____	_____	_____	_____
_____	_____	_____	_____
_____	_____	_____	_____
_____	_____	_____	_____

Opening Lead _____

How the hand was bid:

SOUTH	WEST	NORTH	EAST
1 ♠	Pass	3 ♣	Pass
3 ♡	Pass	4 NT	Pass
5 ◊	Pass	7 ♠	All Pass

Opening lead — ♣ 9

How the hand was played: When this hand was played, South won the first trick in dummy with the king of clubs and drew two rounds of trumps with the ace and king. When the trumps failed to break, South led this other club and held his breath.

Fortunately enough, West had to follow suit. Declarer won in dummy with the ace of clubs and ruffed a club. He next cashed the ace of hearts, ruffed a heart in dummy, ruffed another low club and ruffed his last low heart.

But now dummy was reduced to three diamonds and a good club. Declarer couldn't cash the club because West still had a trump. And if declarer led diamonds, he would have to give a diamond trick to West.

It was not a distinguished performance, and the only thing to be said for it is that West enjoyed it immensely.

ONE TRICK AHEAD

South's trouble was that he got one trick ahead of himself. After winning the second club trick with dummy's ace, South must not immediately ruff a club.

Instead, South takes the ace of hearts and ruffs a heart. Then he ruffs a low club. He ruffs his other low heart with dummy's last trump and ruffs another low club.

This sets up dummy's last club and puts South in his own hand—where he wants to be. He draws the last trump, discarding a diamond from dummy, and cashes the king of hearts to discard another diamond. Then dummy wins the last two tricks with the ace of diamonds and the good club.

Let Others Teach Your Children

"Should a parent teach his children to play bridge?" asks a perplexed reader. "I manage to keep a smile on my face when a stranger bids or plays horribly as my partner, but I blow up when my own flesh and blood does it. Here's the sort of thing that turns my hair prematurely gray."

South dealer   **Both sides vulnerable**

                                    NORTH
                                    ♠ A Q
                                    ♡ 7 6 4
                                    ◇ K Q J 9 3 2
                                    ♣ 7 3

WEST   EAST

♠ J 10 9 8 7 3   ♠ K 6 5
♡ K 8   ♡ J 10 9
◇ 6 4   ◇ 7 5
♣ A 5 2   ♣ 10 9 8 6 4

                                    SOUTH-D
                                    ♠ 4 2
                                    ♡ A Q 5 3 2
                                    ◇ A 10 8
                                    ♣ K Q J

Defense Tricks:

☐ ☐ ☐ ☐ ☐ ☐ ☐ ☐ ☐ ☐ ☐ ☐ ☐ ☐

Bid the hand your way:

North	East	South	West

Opening Lead _____

How the hand was bid:

SOUTH	WEST	NORTH	EAST
1 ♡	1 ♠	2 ◇	Pass
3 ◇	Pass	3 ♡	Pass
4 ♡	All Pass		

Opening lead — ♠ J

How the hand was played: "My college-age daughter, playing the South hand, finessed with dummy's queen of spades at the first trick, losing to the king. Back came a club to the ace and another to the queen.

"Now that unthinking child of mine led a diamond to dummy to try a finesse with the queen of hearts. This lost to the king, and the jack of hearts took the setting trick.

"After all I've told her about using the bidding to locate the missing high cards. I've put the best bridge books in her hand, and I've even read some of them to her. It makes you wonder whether anything is worthwhile!"

SIMPLE REMEDY

There is a simple remedy for this sort of problem: Let somebody else teach your children. A beginner's mistakes bring no tears to the eyes of a stranger.

It's true that South should see that West must have the king of hearts for his overcall (after the spade finesse loses, at any rate). The only chance to drive out the king of hearts without using the queen is to lead out the ace of hearts and then a low heart.

If South tries this desperate play, West does have to play the king of hearts, even though he gets nothing much for it. South can later use the queen of hearts to draw East's last trump, thus making the contract.

To see this kind of play takes the willingness to think. As the old proverb has it: You can read a course to Daughter, but you can't make her think.

Simple Word Defined for Players

Millions of readers have written in to ask for a definition of the word "conservative." That's easy: A bridge hand will give us the answer.

South dealer   **North-South vulnerable**

```
                    NORTH
                    ♠ 5 3
                    ♡ A K 7 5 2
                    ◇ A 9 6
                    ♣ A 7 4
       WEST                        EAST
       ♠ 6 2                       ♠ 8 7 4
       ♡ Q J 10 9 8 6              ♡ None
       ◇ K Q 10                    ◇ J 8 7 5
       ♣ K 6                       ♣ Q J 10 9 8 3
                    SOUTH-D
                    ♠ A K Q J 10 9
                    ♡ 4 3
                    ◇ 4 3 2
                    ♣ 5 2
```

Defense Tricks:

☐ ☐ ☐ ☐ ☐ ☐ ☐ ☐ ☐ ☐ ☐ ☐ ☐

Bid the hand your way:

North	East	South	West
_____	_____	_____	_____
_____	_____	_____	_____
_____	_____	_____	_____
_____	_____	_____	_____

Opening Lead _____

How the hand was bid:

SOUTH	WEST	NORTH	EAST
1 ♠	2 ♡	Double	3 ♣
Pass	Pass	Double	Pass
3 ♠	Pass	4 ♠	All Pass

Opening lead — ♡ Q

How the hand was played: South played the king of hearts from the dummy at the first trick, and East was happy to ruff. South eventually lost two diamonds and a club as well.

Clearly, South was no conservative. A conservative, surely, is somebody who conserves; and South had failed to conserve one of his heart tricks. The correct play is to duck the first heart, letting West win the trick. If West continues with hearts, South ducks the second heart and ruffs the third heart in his own hand. He then draws trumps and gets to dummy to discard losers on the ace and king of hearts.

CONSERVATIVES CONVERSE

"Why did you play the king of hearts?" West asked declarer. "I'm a conservative bidder, so I surely had a six-card heart suit."

"Some conservative," East scoffed. "They'd lead three rounds of spades, and you'd have to ruff high. That would cost you three trump tricks, so you'd be down two. But I'm a conservative. I'd have made three clubs."

"A conservative analyst!" South put in. "We'd lead two rounds of trumps, and you'd have to lose three spades and two aces."

"I didn't bid conservatively," North sadly admitted. "I could have passed three spades or bid three notrump. But you had 150 honors, so we made a profit of 50 points on the hand. When you're my partner, any profit at all is a good result. If we win on every hand, we can't lose very much."

So now you know what a conservative is.

Bargain Hunter Pays through Nose

If you haggle over a price that you can afford to pay, you will get many bargains but you will often wind up paying through the nose. Long experience has taught me that some bridge players have noses for no other reason.

South dealer   **Both sides vulnerable**

NORTH
♠ A 10 6
♡ J 10
♢ K Q 7 6 5 2
♣ Q 4

WEST   EAST
♠ 9 7 2   ♠ 8 5 4 3
♡ Q 9 7 5 2   ♡ 8 6 3
♢ 10 3   ♢ A J 9
♣ A 10 9   ♣ K 8 7

SOUTH-D
♠ K Q J
♡ A K 4
♢ 8 4
♣ J 6 5 3 2

Defense Tricks:

☐ ☐ ☐ ☐ ☐ ☐ ☐ ☐ ☐ ☐ ☐ ☐ ☐

Bid the hand your way:

North	East	South	West
_____	_____	_____	_____
_____	_____	_____	_____
_____	_____	_____	_____
		Opening Lead _____	

How the hand was bid:

SOUTH	WEST	NORTH	EAST
1 ♣	Pass	1 ♢	Pass
1 NT	Pass	3 NT	All Pass

Opening lead — ♡ 5

How the hand was played: Declarer won the first trick in dummy with the ten of hearts and led a spade to the king in order to begin the diamonds from his own hand. It was a case of taking pains to make the wrong play.

When South led a diamond, West signalled with the ten. Declarer played the king from dummy, and East carefully played the nine. This proper play doomed South.

Declarer returned to his hand with the queen of spades and led his other diamond, still hoping to win all but one of dummy's long suit. He wound up with only one diamond trick.

East won the second diamond and returned a heart. Now South could not lead diamonds from his own hand. He could get to dummy with the ace of spades to set up the diamonds but could never get back to cash them. After a long struggle, South managed to get seven tricks. Down two.

CAN LOSE TWO DIAMONDS

South could well afford to lose two diamond tricks and should have done so. There was no harm in leading the first diamond from the South hand provided that declarer played a low diamond from dummy instead of the king. It would be just as good and somewhat simpler if declarer led a low diamond from dummy at the second trick instead of bothering to get to his own hand.

East would win the first diamond trick and lead a heart to South's ace. Declarer could now lead a diamond to dummy's king, losing to the ace. By this time the rest of dummy's diamonds would be good, and the ace of spades would serve as an entry to them.

Look Gift Horse in the Mouth

The etiquette books tell you not to look too closely at a gift, and the chapter for polite bridge players says to pay your losses in clean, crisp money. There's no need for a chapter on how to accept money, because a polite bridge player is a born loser.

South dealer   **North-South vulnerable**

NORTH
- ♠ K 4
- ♡ K J 10
- ◇ 7 2
- ♣ A K J 8 6 3

<table>
<tr><td>

WEST
- ♠ 7 6 3
- ♡ Q 8 5 3 2
- ◇ A Q 3
- ♣ 7 5

</td><td>

EAST
- ♠ 8 5
- ♡ 9 7 6
- ◇ 10 9 8 4
- ♣ Q 10 9 2

</td></tr>
</table>

SOUTH-D
- ♠ A Q J 10 9 2
- ♡ A 4
- ◇ K J 6 5
- ♣ 4

Defense Tricks:

☐ ☐ ☐ ☐ ☐ ☐ ☐ ☐ ☐ ☐ ☐ ☐

Bid the hand your way:

North	East	South	West
_____	_____	_____	_____
_____	_____	_____	_____
_____	_____	_____	_____
_____	_____	_____	_____
		Opening Lead	_____

How the hand was bid:

SOUTH	WEST	NORTH	EAST
1 ♠	Pass	2 ♣	Pass
3 ♠	Pass	5 ♠	Pass
6 ♠	All Pass		

Opening lead — ♡ 3

How the hand was played: West opened the three of hearts, declarer played the ten from dummy and East naturally played low. Delighted at this "gift" of a trick, South played the low heart from his hand. He even remembered his childhood training in time to give West a grateful smile.

Declarer next drew three rounds of trumps, cashed the ace of hearts and led to dummy's king of clubs to discard two diamonds on the ace of clubs and king of hearts. But he still had the K-J of diamonds and had to lose both of them to West. Down one.

SHOULD REFUSE GIFT

South should refuse the gift by winning the first trick with the ace of hearts. He draws one trump with the queen, leads a club to the king and ruffs a club high.

When both opponents play clubs on this trick, South's slam is sure. He leads his low trump to dummy's king and ruffs another low club.

Now South can draw the last trump and get back to dummy by leading his carefully preserved low heart to dummy's king. The ace of clubs then drops the queen, and the last two clubs are also good. South gets rid of three diamonds and can afford to give up one diamond trick.

The point is that South starts the hand with ten sure tricks and should play for two extra clubs rather than just one extra heart. If either opponent discards on the second round of clubs, South is in position to draw trumps and lead his low heart for a finesse of dummy's jack. He can then take two discards and try for a diamond trick.

Students Should Detect Culprit

All students of crime should examine this hand. It is possible to detect the criminal and his crime without bloodhounds or magnifying glass.

South dealer   **Both sides vulnerable**

NORTH
♠ K Q J 4
♡ 8 7 3
◇ J 5 2
♣ K 6 5

WEST
♠ 8 7 6 3 2
♡ None
◇ 10 9 8 7
♣ Q 9 8 2

EAST
♠ A 10 9
♡ 9 6 4
◇ Q 6 4 3
♣ A 10 7

SOUTH-D
♠ 5
♡ A K Q J 10 5 2
◇ A K
♣ J 4 3

Defense Tricks:

☐ ☐ ☐ ☐ ☐ ☐ ☐ ☐ ☐ ☐ ☐ ☐ ☐

Bid the hand your way:

North	East	South	West
____	____	____	____
____	____	____	____
____	____	____	____
____	____	____	____

Opening Lead ____

How the hand was bid:

SOUTH	WEST	NORTH	EAST
2 ♡	Pass	2 ♠	Pass
3 ♡	Pass	3 NT	Pass
4 ♡	All Pass		

Opening lead — ◊ 10

How the hand was played: South won the first trick with the king of diamonds, drew three rounds of trumps and led a spade to force out the ace. East returned a diamond to the ace, and South led a club, losing dummy's king to the ace. Back came the queen of diamonds, and South ruffed.

South led out two more rounds of trumps but then had to lose two more club tricks. Down one.

You can probably name the criminal without even stopping to think, but can you say exactly where he went wrong? Decide for yourself before you read on.

REASONABLE CONTRACT

South was the criminal, but don't blame him for the bidding. It's quite true that South would make nine tricks at notrump without even breathing hard, but four hearts was a perfectly reasonable contract—and unbeatable if South thinks before he plays.

After drawing just one round of trumps, South must stop. He switches to spades, losing dummy's jack to the ace. Back comes a diamond to the ace, and South is home if he can get to dummy to cash the two spades.

South can force an entry to dummy in trumps. He leads a low trump, losing dummy's seven to the nine. Back comes the queen of diamonds, and South ruffs with an honor. Then he leads his remaining low trump to dummy's eight. He is in position to discard two clubs on the king and the queen of spades.

Don't Play While You're Thinking

Experts differ on the right way to think at the bridge table. some favor rubbing the chin, a few uncouth types recommend scratching the head and the old-fashioned school speak very warmly about gazing at the ceiling. All of them agree on one principle: Don't go on playing while you're thinking.

North dealer   **North-South vulnerable**

NORTH-D
- ♠ K J 5
- ♡ 4 3
- ◇ A 8 7 3
- ♣ A K 10 7

WEST
- ♠ 8 7 4
- ♡ 10 9 8 5 2
- ◇ 9 5 4 2
- ♣ 6

EAST
- ♠ A Q 6
- ♡ None
- ◇ K Q J 10 6
- ♣ Q 8 4 3 2

SOUTH
- ♠ 10 9 3 2
- ♡ A K Q J 7 6
- ◇ None
- ♣ J 9 5

Defense Tricks:

☐ ☐ ☐ ☐ ☐ ☐ ☐ ☐ ☐ ☐ ☐ ☐ ☐

Bid the hand your way:

North	East	South	West
_____	_____	_____	_____
_____	_____	_____	_____
_____	_____	_____	_____
_____	_____	_____	_____

Opening Lead _____

How the hand was bid:

NORTH	EAST	SOUTH	WEST
1 ♣	1 ◇	1 ♡	Pass
1 NT	Pass	4 ♡	All Pass

Opening lead — ◇ 2

How the hand was played: Declarer won the first trick with dummy's ace of diamonds, discarding a club from his hand. He then led a trump, and East discarded a club.

South won the first round of trumps with the ace of hearts and a frown. Clearly the bad news called for thought, but no idea occurred to South. To pass the time he led out the king and then the queen of trumps.

South's first round of trumps was proper and normal. The second round was fatal because it removed the remaining trump from dummy.

When declarer lost a spade to the queen, a diamond return made him trump; and when he lost a spade to the ace, another diamond made him ruff again.

LOW IN TRUMPS

By this time, South had only one trump, and West had two. South cashed one spade, but West ruffed the last spade and led a fourth diamond to force out the jack of trumps. West's last trump took the setting trick.

South makes the contract if he switches to spades after just one round of trumps. East gets his two spade tricks and returns a diamond each time, forcing South to ruff with the six and seven. South cashes a spade and leads his last spade to discard dummy's last diamond.

West ruffs and returns his fourth diamond, but dummy's remaining trump makes all the difference. Declarer ruffs in dummy and discards a second club from his hand. He can cash the ace of clubs and then take the last three tricks with the K-Q-J of trumps.

Wrong Trump Play Leads to Trouble

One of my closest friends begins the play of each hand by drawing trumps. I once asked him his reason for this habit, and he gave me his answer: "If a fire should break out, at least I'd have the trumps drawn."

North dealer   **North-South vulnerable**

NORTH-D

- ♠ A 7 3
- ♡ A J 7 6
- ◇ 8 7 4
- ♣ A Q J

WEST	EAST
♠ 4	♠ 8 6 5 2
♡ K 8	♡ Q 10 9 3
◇ Q J 10 9 5 3	◇ K 6 2
♣ 8 4 3 2	♣ K 7

SOUTH

- ♠ K Q J 10 9
- ♡ 5 4 2
- ◇ A
- ♣ 10 9 6 5

Defense Tricks:

☐ ☐ ☐ ☐ ☐ ☐ ☐ ☐ ☐ ☐ ☐ ☐ ☐

Bid the hand your way:

North	East	South	West
_____	_____	_____	_____
_____	_____	_____	_____
_____	_____	_____	_____
		Opening Lead	_____

How the hand was bid:

NORTH	EAST	SOUTH	WEST
1 NT	Pass	3 ♠	Pass
4 ♠	All Pass		

Opening lead — ◇ Q

How the hand was played: Not long ago he had this hand to play. He won the first trick with the ace of diamonds and drew four rounds of trumps.

You might think I was holding my breath since I was the dummy and could see that my partner was headed for trouble. You would be wrong. When you play bridge with a confirmed trump-drawer, you don't have enough breath to bother holding it.

After drawing trumps, South tried the club finesse. East won with the king of clubs and returned a diamond to force out declarer's last trump.

BLOCKED CLUBS

South could take dummy's ace and queen of clubs, but couldn't get back to his hand for the ten of clubs. He got five spades, two clubs and the two red aces. Fortunately, we had honors, so we didn't lose anything except time.

Of course you can see the correct line of play. South wins the first diamond and draws two rounds of trumps with the ace and king in that order. When the bad break shows up, South wants to be in his own hand to try the club finesse.

East takes the king of clubs and returns a diamond to make South ruff. Declarer leads a club to dummy's queen and the draws two more rounds of trumps. On the fourth trump, South discards dummy's ace of clubs.

This unblocks the suit so that South can cash the ten and nine of clubs to score game and rubber. And then if a fire should break out, South would be about 900 points better off than if he had drawn trumps to begin with.

Best Bargain: Give Opponents Nothing

It's a fine idea to win a trick with a high card, but it's even better to capture an opponent's high card while you're winning your trick. Likewise, when you cannot avoid losing a trick, give up as little as possible in the process.

North dealer   **North-South vulnerable**

NORTH-D

♠ A K
♡ K J 10 8 7 4 2
◇ A
♣ K 7 4

WEST

♠ 9 8 5 2
♡ 5
◇ J 9 6 5 4
♣ 10 8 3

EAST

♠ 10 6 4
♡ Q 9 6 3
◇ 10 8 7 3 2
♣ A

SOUTH

♠ Q J 7 3
♡ A
◇ K Q
♣ Q J 9 6 5 2

Defense Tricks:

☐ ☐ ☐ ☐ ☐ ☐ ☐ ☐ ☐ ☐ ☐ ☐ ☐

Bid the hand your way:

North	East	South	West
_____	_____	_____	_____
_____	_____	_____	_____
_____	_____	_____	_____
_____	_____	_____	_____

Opening Lead _____

How the hand was bid:

NORTH	EAST	SOUTH	WEST
1 ♡	Pass	2 ♣	Pass
3 ♡	Pass	3 ♠	Pass
4 ♣	Pass	6 ♣	All Pass
			Opening lead — ♡ 5

How the hand was played: West led the five of hearts, an obvious singleton. South won with the ace of hearts and saw the importance of drawing West's trumps. Declarer led a low club from his hand, losing dummy's king to the ace.

East returned a heart, and South's cause was hopeless. If he ruffed low, West would overruff; if South ruffed with the jack of clubs, West would eventually win a trick with the ten of clubs.

When West took the setting trick with the ten of clubs, North muttered under his breath. Since a dummy's best friend is his mutter, we can report that North merely remarked that not all the butchers are in the meat business.

"How could I tell the ace of clubs was blank?" South asked. "If I played a low club from dummy and lost to the ten or eight, you'd be crying your eyes out."

NO NEED TO PEEK

Dummy subsided, but not because South was right. After winning the first trick with the ace of hearts, South should not immediately lead trumps. Instead, he should lead a diamond to dummy's ace and return a low trump from dummy.

East is obliged to play the ace of clubs, and South can follow suit with a low trump, saving his own Q-J and dummy's king. When East then returns a heart, South can well afford to step up with the queen of trumps. He has his own jack and dummy's king to draw the two remaining trumps.

Imitation Improves on Nature

Every man whose wife wants a mink coat should be interested in a proof that an imitation is sometimes better than the real thing. Thus far my research into the matter has gone only as far as a bridge hand, but this does serve to demonstrate the general principle.

South dealer   **Neither side vulnerable**

NORTH

♠ 7 5 2
♡ 10 8 4 3
◇ A 6 3
♣ Q 8 2

WEST

♠ K 8 6 4 3
♡ J 7
◇ 9 2
♣ A 9 5 3

EAST

♠ J 10 9
♡ 6 2
◇ Q J 10 8
♣ K 7 6 4

SOUTH-D

♠ A Q
♡ A K Q 9 5
◇ K 7 5 4
♣ J 10

Defense Tricks:

☐ ☐ ☐ ☐ ☐ ☐ ☐ ☐ ☐ ☐ ☐ ☐ ☐ ☐

Bid the hand your way:

North	East	South	West
————	————	————	————
————	————	————	————
————	————	————	————
————	————	————	————
		Opening Lead ————	

How the hand was bid:

SOUTH	WEST	NORTH	EAST
1 ♡	Pass	2 ♡	Pass
4 ♡	All Pass		

Opening lead — ◇ 9

How the hand was played: South saw that he could take a real finesse in spades whenever he pleased. If it worked, he would make his contract, losing only one diamond and two clubs. Instead of trying his genuine finesse, South relied on an imitation.

Declarer won the first trick in dummy with the ace of diamonds and returned a low club. To East, it seemed that declarer was about to try a club finesse.

Deceived by his imitation finesse, East played a low club. South played the jack to force out the ace, and only then did East see that the club play was a fake.

West led his other diamond, and South won with the king. Declarer now led out the ace and king of hearts and was delighted to see that the trumps broke evenly.

SETS UP QUEEN

South could afford to lead the ten of clubs, losing to the king. This set up dummy's queen of clubs.

East returned the jack of spades, but it was too late. Since declarer had no further need of the spade finesse, he put up the ace of spades, led a small trump to dummy and discarded the queen of spades on dummy's queen of clubs.

Declarer could then give up a diamond trick and ruff his remaining diamond with dummy's last trump. The defenders could get only one diamond and two clubs.

If South relied on the genuine finesse in spades, he would lose a spade trick as well as a diamond and two clubs. The fake finesse in clubs was better than the genuine article.

Don't Stop Counting after Bidding

During the auction, you count your points and add them to the points shown by your partner's bids. The total tells you how high your side can afford to bid. Keep counting after the auction has ended; you may find out how high to play.

South dealer   **Neither side vulnerable**

                        NORTH
                        ♠ Q J 8
                        ♡ A 8
                        ◇ K J 6 4
                        ♣ J 10 5 2

        WEST   EAST
        ♠ 10 9 4   ♠ 7 6 3 2
        ♡ J 9 7 6 3   ♡ K 10 5
        ◇ 5 2   ◇ A 8 7
        ♣ 7 4 3   ♣ A 9 6

                        SOUTH-D
                        ♠ A K 5
                        ♡ Q 4 2
                        ◇ Q 10 9 3
                        ♣ K Q 8

Defense Tricks:

☐ ☐ ☐ ☐ ☐ ☐ ☐ ☐ ☐ ☐ ☐ ☐ ☐

Bid the hand your way:

North	East	South	West
_____	_____	_____	_____
_____	_____	_____	_____
_____	_____	_____	_____
_____	_____	_____	_____

Opening Lead _____

94

How the hand was bid:

SOUTH	WEST	NORTH	EAST
1 NT	Pass	3 NT	All Pass

Opening lead — ♡ 6

How the hand was played: West opened the six of hearts, and declarer correctly played low from dummy. East played . . . well, what did he play?

East counted 12 points in the dummy and 11 points in his own hand. Since the deck contains only 40 points, South and West had 17 points between them. South needed 16 points for his bid, so West could have 1 point at most.

East next used the Rule of Eleven, subtracting the opening lead from 11. The remainder, 5, told him that dummy, East and South held five cards higher than the six of hearts. Dummy held two of those five cards, and East held two; so South could have only one heart higher than the six.

The counting process took only a few seconds because East was used to it. East then knew that South's hearts were headed by the queen and West's by the jack.

DRIVES OUT QUEEN

East played the ten of hearts at the first trick, and South had to win with the queen for fear of not getting a second heart trick if he failed to take it. Declarer next led the ten of diamonds, hoping to steal one trick, but East took the ace of diamonds at once and shot back the king of hearts to dummy's ace.

South could get only eight tricks outside of clubs. As soon as declarer led clubs, East took the ace and led his last heart to give West three heart tricks. Down one.

The counting and planning were necessary to defeat the contract. If East wins the first trick with the king of hearts, South still gets two heart tricks, but the defenders get only one. South makes ten tricks instead of only eight.

Bad Play May Not Be Fatal

You don't automatically go down just because you adopt the wrong line of play; the opponents may throw the hand right back to you. This is even better than playing the hand properly; you can have the fun of reminding them that you gave them a sporting chance to beat you.

North dealer   **Both sides vulnerable**

NORTH-D

♠ A 3
♡ A 10 4
◇ K Q 9 8 6 2
♣ 9 6

WEST	EAST
♠ Q 9 4	♠ K 8 7
♡ 9 8 6 5	♡ J 7
◇ 7	◇ J 10 4 3
♣ Q 10 8 5 3	♣ K J 4 2

SOUTH

♠ J 10 6 5 2
♡ K Q 3 2
◇ A 5
♣ A 7

Defense Tricks:

☐ ☐ ☐ ☐ ☐ ☐ ☐ ☐ ☐ ☐ ☐ ☐ ☐

Bid the hand your way:

North	East	South	West
___	___	___	___
___	___	___	___
___	___	___	___
	___	___	___

Opening Lead _____

96

How the hand was bid:

NORTH	EAST	SOUTH	WEST
1 ◇	Pass	1 ♠	Pass
2 ◇	Pass	2 ♡	Pass
3 ◇	Pass	3 NT	All Pass

Opening lead — ♣ 5

How the hand was played: South won the first club trick, cashed the ace of diamonds and led his low diamond toward dummy. West thereupon went into the grandfather of all huddles.

West couldn't spare a club since he might need all of his clubs to defeat the contract. He was afraid to discard a spade since South had bid the suit and might be able to run the entire suit after one discard.

After much agonizing, West discarded a heart. South thereupon cashed the three top hearts and thus set up his last heart. This turned out to be his ninth trick.

SHOULD THROW SPADE

West should throw a spade on the second diamond. This is safe if East has the king or jack of spades. Even if South has K-J-x-x-x of spades, he may lose a finesse to West's queen if West discards his lowest spade without excessive distress.

If West keeps his hearts, South can get only three heart tricks. Declarer can cash the ace and king of hearts to drop the jack and can then lead a heart to dummy's ten, but he cannot get back to his own hand to cash the queen of hearts.

There is no need for South to offer West this sporting chance. South should start on the hearts immediately, cashing the ace and king before touching the diamonds. When the jack of hearts drops, declarer can lead to the ten and return to his hand with the ace of diamonds to cash the queen of hearts.

97

Good Kibitzer Does Not Volunteer

Most bridge writers tell you how to bid or play well, but who else gives you rules for good kibitzing? The first rule is familiar to anybody who has served in the army: Don't volunteer.

South dealer   **North-South vulnerable**

```
                    NORTH
                    ♠ 7 4 3
                    ♡ 9 3
                    ◇ A Q 8 7 4
                    ♣ K 6 3
        WEST                        EAST
        ♠ K Q 10 9 5                ♠ 8 6
        ♡ Q J 10 4                  ♡ K 8 7 6 2
        ◇ 6 3                       ◇ K 5
        ♣ 8 4                       ♣ 9 7 5 2
                    SOUTH-D
                    ♠ A J 2
                    ♡ A 5
                    ◇ J 10 9 2
                    ♣ A Q J 10
```

Defense Tricks:

☐ ☐ ☐ ☐ ☐ ☐ ☐ ☐ ☐ ☐ ☐ ☐ ☐

Bid the hand your way:

North	East	South	West
_____	_____	_____	_____
_____	_____	_____	_____
_____	_____	_____	_____
_____	_____	_____	_____

Opening Lead _____

How the hand was bid:

SOUTH	WEST	NORTH	EAST
1 NT	Pass	3 NT	All Pass

Opening lead — ♠ K

How the hand was played: You are sitting behind South, watching him play the hand at three notrump. He plays the deuce of spades on the first trick, hoping that West will lead another spade. West glares suspiciously at South and switches to the queen of hearts.

South takes the ace of hearts and his four clubs but then has to try the diamond finesse. The defenders collect a diamond and four hearts in addition to the first spade.

South shakes his head dolefully. "Just as bad if I take the first spade," he comments. "When I lose the diamond finesse they take four spade tricks."

DANGEROUS MOMENT

This is your dangerous moment. It would be most unprofessional to volunteer the statement that South played the hand badly. Just clear your throat and lift your eyebrows.

Once they ask you what you have on your mind, you must follow the second rule for kibitzers: Be kind to the culprit. Don't say "The idiot goofed." Say: "There's a way to make the hand, but only a real bridge player would see it."

Then you can point out that South should play the jack of spades at the first trick. West will naturally believe that South started with the doubleton A-J.

It seems safe for West to continue spades, and this time South takes the ace. When South loses the diamond finesse, East cannot return a spade.

Be sure to read all my books to learn how much insurance to carry and what a kibitzer should know about curing black eyes.

If You're Getting Out, Lock the Doors

It isn't always enough to know the standard safety plays. You may have to take other precautions to make your contract.

North dealer   **East-West vulnerable**

NORTH-D
♠ K 9 5 2
♡ A J 8 7 5
◇ A K
♣ K 4

WEST	EAST
♠ Q 10 8 7	♠ None
♡ 6	♡ K Q 10 9 4 2
◇ 8 7 4 3	◇ 9 5 2
♣ Q J 10 9	♣ 8 7 6 3

SOUTH
♠ A J 6 4 3
♡ 3
◇ Q J 10 6
♣ A 5 2

Defense Tricks:

☐ ☐ ☐ ☐ ☐ ☐ ☐ ☐ ☐ ☐ ☐ ☐ ☐

Bid the hand your way:

North	East	South	West
――――	――――	――――	――――
――――	――――	――――	――――
――――	――――	――――	――――
――――	――――	――――	――――

Opening Lead _____

How the hand was bid:

NORTH	EAST	SOUTH	WEST
1 ♡	Pass	1 ♠	Pass
4 ♠	Pass	4 NT	Pass
5 ♡	Pass	5 NT	Pass
6 ♠	Pass	Pass	All Pass

Opening lead — ♣ Q

How the hand was played: West opened the queen of clubs, and declarer won in dummy with the king. Declarer led a low trump from dummy to his own ace. If East held all four trumps, South could lead a trump to the king and, eventually, lead a trump through East's Q-10 to South's jack.

Since it was West who had all four trumps, South next led a low trump toward dummy. West put in the ten, and dummy's king won. South now had to postpone further trump plays. First he had to cash the ace of clubs and ruff his losing club in dummy.

STILL TOO EARLY

Even then South could not afford to resume trump leads. West would take the queen of trumps and lead a club to make South ruff. South would be able to draw West's last trump, but the diamonds would then be blocked.

Declarer avoided this trap by cashing the ace and king of diamonds before leading the nine of spades from dummy. It was a good start, but not quite good enough.

West took the queen of spades and led his singleton heart to dummy's ace. Since dummy had nothing but hearts, declarer had to lead a heart from dummy—and now he could not shut out West's eight of trumps.

South led the nine of spades from dummy one trick too early. He should cash not only the top diamonds but also the ace of hearts. Then he can lead the nine of spades to West's queen. Any return puts South in his own hand. He can safely draw the last trump and cash his good diamonds.

Be Patient with Good Partner

"You are very polite and patient," a kibitzer told me recently at a tournament (much to my surprise). "Your partner just threw a trick away, and you congratulated him for his beautiful play."

South dealer   **Neither side vulnerable**

NORTH
♠ A 9 6 3
♡ 10 6 3
◇ K 7 4
♣ A Q 9

WEST
♠ K J 4 2
♡ 9 8
◇ Q 8 5
♣ J 8 7 3

EAST
♠ 10 8 7 5
♡ 7 5 2
◇ J 10 9 6
♣ 10 4

SOUTH-D
♠ Q
♡ A K Q J 4
◇ A 3 2
♣ K 6 5 2

Defense Tricks:

☐ ☐ ☐ ☐ ☐ ☐ ☐ ☐ ☐ ☐ ☐ ☐

Bid the hand your way:

North	East	South	West
_____	_____	_____	_____
_____	_____	_____	_____
_____	_____	_____	_____

Opening Lead _____

How the hand was bid:

SOUTH	WEST	NORTH	EAST
1 ♡	Pass	2 NT	Pass
6 ♡	All Pass		

Opening lead — ♣ 3

How the hand was played: My partner won the first trick with the ace of clubs and drew two rounds of trumps with the ace and king. Then he abandoned trumps leaving one trump still in the East hand.

Declarer took the queen of clubs and led the low club toward his hand. East pounced on this trick with his small trump, and my kibitzer snorted with disgust. These new players couldn't even count trumps!

East returned the jack of diamonds to declarer's ace, and South cashed the king of clubs to discard a low diamond from dummy. Eventually he ruffed his losing diamond in dummy, making the slam.

UNDESERVED

The kibitzer's compliment was undeserved, because my politeness was with the kibitzer, not with my partner. South did not throw a trick away by leaving a trump out; drawing trumps would cost him the slam.

Suppose South draws three trumps. Then he must lose a club and a diamond. What can he do with those losers?

When East ruffed on the third round of clubs, he got only a club that was of no use to South. As the play went, this did not help the defense. If East failed to ruff, it would be just as bad. South would take the king of clubs and ruff his last club with dummy's ten of hearts. Then South would get back to his hand to draw the last trump and would eventually lose a diamond.

103

Play with Odds—Not against Them

When the opponents hold two high cards, the odds are 3 to 1 that at least one of them will be in favorable position—assuming that each of the cards has an even chance to be in favorable or unfavorable position. For example, if you take two finesses, the odds are 3 to 1 in favor of winning at least one of them.

South dealer   **Both sides vulnerable**

```
                      NORTH
                      ♠ K 6 2
                      ♡ A 3 2
                      ◊ K 6 4
                      ♣ Q J 10 9
       WEST                            EAST
       ♠ Q J 10 9                      ♠ 7 4 3
       ♡ 6 4                           ♡ 7 5
       ◊ J 8                           ◊ Q 10 9 7
       ♣ K 7 4 3 2                     ♣ A 8 6 5
                      SOUTH-D
                      ♠ A 8 5
                      ♡ K Q J 10 9 8
                      ◊ A 5 3 2
                      ♣ None
```

Defense Tricks:

☐ ☐ ☐ ☐ ☐ ☐ ☐ ☐ ☐ ☐ ☐ ☐ ☐ ☐

Bid the hand your way:

North	East	South	West
_____	_____	_____	_____
_____	_____	_____	_____
_____	_____	_____	_____
_____	_____	_____	_____
		Opening Lead	_____

How the hand was bid:

SOUTH	WEST	NORTH	EAST
1 ♡	Pass	2 NT	Pass
6 ♡	All Pass		

Opening lead — ♠ Q

How the hand was played: South won the first spade, drew two rounds of trumps and led out three rounds of diamonds in the hope that his last diamond would become set up.

If the diamonds broke 3-3, South could discard dummy's losing spade on his last diamond. Since the odds were almost 2 to 1 against so favorable a diamond break, South had no reason to complain when his plan failed.

South had to lose a spade as well as the diamond. He had to be satisfied with the honors to avoid losing points on his fine hand.

RUFFING FINESSE

Declarer should win the first trick in dummy with the king of spades and returns the queen of clubs. South intends to throw a loser if East plays low, but to ruff if East plays high.

If East plays the ace, South ruffs and draws trumps. He gets to dummy with the ace of trumps to resume the clubs. East plays low, of course, and South discards a loser. West can win the trick, but declarer gets back to dummy with the king of diamonds to discard his other losers on the good clubs.

If East plays low on the first round of clubs, South throws a loser at once. West can win that trick, but South wins any return and draws trumps, ending in the dummy. He then leads the jack of clubs—once more planning to discard losers if East plays low but to ruff if East puts up the ace.

South makes the slam if East has one or both of the top clubs. He goes down only if West has both of the high clubs.

Take a Chance When You Must

Only one bridge player in a thousand would make game in the hand shown below, but the principle of play is very simple. It's just a matter of seeing what you need and then taking a chance.

South dealer   **East-West vulnerable**

```
                        NORTH
                        ♠ 10 7 3 2
                        ♡ A Q 10
                        ◇ K 5 4
                        ♣ 8 4 3

        WEST                              EAST
        ♠ None                            ♠ Q 6 5 4
        ♡ J 8 5 3                         ♡ 9 7 4
        ◇ Q J 10 9 3                      ◇ A 8 7
        ♣ A 9 5 2                         ♣ Q 7 6

                        SOUTH-D
                        ♠ A K J 9 8
                        ♡ K 6 2
                        ◇ 6 2
                        ♣ K J 10
```

Defense Tricks:

☐ ☐ ☐ ☐ ☐ ☐ ☐ ☐ ☐ ☐ ☐ ☐ ☐

Bid the hand your way:

North	East	South	West
_____	_____	_____	_____
_____	_____	_____	_____
_____	_____	_____	_____
_____	_____	_____	_____

Opening Lead _____

How the hand was bid:

SOUTH	WEST	NORTH	EAST
1 ♠	Pass	2 ♠	Pass
3 ♠	Pass	4 ♠	All Pass

Opening lead — ◊ Q

How the hand was played: When the hand was played, West opened the queen of diamonds and continued the suit until South ruffed the third round. South laid down the ace of spades and winced when West discarded a diamond.

Shaking his head dolefully, South led a heart to dummy's queen and returned the ten of spades. East played low, and the ten held the trick. Declarer then led another spade from dummy to win a finesse with the jack.

Now South led his other low heart. West thoughtfully put up the jack, and dummy's ace won. Declarer was in the dummy for the last time and couldn't handle the clubs.

When South led a club from dummy and finessed with the jack, he was allowed to win the trick. He could draw the last trump but sooner or later had to lead clubs from his own hand, allowing the opponents to take two club tricks.

MUST THINK

South must stop to think when the bad trump break shows up. He must get to dummy once for a spade finesse and twice more for club finesses. He therefore needs three entries to dummy—and they are all there in hearts, provided that South is quick to make up his mind.

Declarer must begin the hearts by leading a low heart and trying a finesse with dummy's ten. When this finesse works, South has his three entries to dummy.

Declarer leads the ten of spades from dummy and continues with another spade to the jack. Back to dummy with the queen of hearts for a finesse of the club jack; and back to dummy with the ace of hearts for a finesse again in clubs.

Detectives Should Solve Crime

Bridge detectives are urged to don their deerstalker caps and polish up their magnifying glasses. The clues to a horrible bridge crime—or, possibly, a mishap—are contained in the following account.

North dealer   **North-South vulnerable**

NORTH-D
- ♠ Q 10 9 2
- ♡ Q 9 5
- ◊ A 6 4
- ♣ A 9 4

WEST
- ♠ 5 4
- ♡ 10 8 4 2
- ◊ Q 7 3
- ♣ 6 5 3 2

EAST
- ♠ 6 3
- ♡ A K J 6
- ◊ 10 8 5 2
- ♣ K 8 7

SOUTH
- ♠ A K J 8 7
- ♡ 7 3
- ◊ K J 9
- ♣ Q J 10

Defense Tricks:

☐ ☐ ☐ ☐ ☐ ☐ ☐ ☐ ☐ ☐ ☐ ☐ ☐

Bid the hand your way:

North	East	South	West
_____	_____	_____	_____
_____	_____	_____	_____
_____	_____	_____	_____
_____	_____	_____	_____

Opening Lead _____

How the hand was bid:

NORTH	EAST	SOUTH	WEST
Pass	Pass	1 ♠	Pass
3 ♠	Pass	4 ♠	All Pass
			Opening lead — ♡ 2

How the hand was played: East won the first trick with the jack of hearts and continued with the king and ace. South ruffed the third heart, drew two rounds of trumps and lost the club finesse to the king.

East returned a club, and declarer led a diamond to the ace and returned a diamond to finesse with the jack. West's queen of diamonds took the setting trick.

Was South a criminal, or was it just a case of misleading circumstantial evidence?

COMPULSORY BID

By the time South got around to playing the diamonds, he knew that East's original hand contained the A-K-J of hearts, the king of clubs and only two spades. This came to 11 points in high cards and 1 for the doubleton.

If East also held the queen of diamonds, his count would have been 14 points, enough for a "compulsory" opening bid. But East passed. Therefore he could not hold the queen of diamonds.

With the queen of diamonds thus marked in the West hand, South had only one chance—to find the ten of diamonds in the East hand. (West could not have the doubleton Q-10 of diamonds because the play marked him with at least three diamonds.)

The correct play under these circumstances is to begin with the jack of diamonds from the South hand. West must cover (otherwise South lets the jack ride), and dummy's ace wins. Now declarer leads a diamond from dummy to win a finesse with the nine of diamonds.

Beware Greeks Bearing Gifts

The defenders can often gain an advantage by forcing declarer to accept a trick before he can make full use of it. If declarer refuses this Greek gift, the play may take the odd form of each side trying to thrust a trick on the other side.

East dealer   **East-West vulnerable**

```
                        NORTH
                        ♠ Q 5 2
                        ♡ 8
                        ◇ 6 4 3 2
                        ♣ Q J 10 7 3

        WEST                            EAST-D
        ♠ 9 8 7                         ♠ K J 10
        ♡ Q 9 6 3 2                     ♡ A K J 7 4
        ◇ 8                             ◇ J 10 9
        ♣ 9 6 4 2                       ♣ 8 5

                        SOUTH
                        ♠ A 6 4 3
                        ♡ 10 5
                        ◇ A K Q 7 5
                        ♣ A K
```

Defense Tricks:

☐ ☐ ☐ ☐ ☐ ☐ ☐ ☐ ☐ ☐ ☐ ☐ ☐ ☐

Bid the hand your way:

North	East	South	West
_____	_____	_____	_____
_____	_____	_____	_____
_____	_____	_____	_____
		Opening Lead _____	

How the hand was bid:

EAST	SOUTH	WEST	NORTH
1 ♡	Double	2 ♡	Pass
Pass	3 ◇	Pass	4 ◇
Pass	5 ◇	All Pass	

Opening lead — ♡ 3

How the hand was played: West opened the three of hearts, and East won with the king. Since West had clearly led his fourth-highest heart, East knew that South had another heart and could eventually ruff it in the dummy.

East could see that South held all the missing high cards and that he would easily make the contract if he were allowed to ruff the heart at a time of his own choosing. The best chance of the defense was to make South ruff the heart prematurely.

When East returned the ace of hearts as the second trick, declarer had his chance to ruff the trick in dummy. If he did so, however, he would go down. He would have no way to reach the dummy for the clubs, and he would therefore lose two spades in addition to the first heart trick.

HANDS IT BACK

South worked this out and came to the correct conclusion: He didn't want to ruff that second trick. He discarded a spade from dummy, handing the trick back to East.

East couldn't gain by leading another heart, so he shifted to a club. There was still the chance that South had A-K-Q-8-7 of diamonds, in which case he would not be able to get to dummy with a trump.

As it happened, South had the five of diamonds—a card of great value precisely because it was so low. South won the club return, drew three rounds of trumps, got the other high club out of the way and then led the five of diamonds to dummy's six. This enabled him to run the rest of the clubs, discarding his three low spades.

Don't Study Odds, Study the Hand

If you study the odds carefully, you can explain to your partner just how unlucky you are. If you spend the same amount of effort on playing the cards properly, the complaint about hard luck will come from the opponents.

South dealer   **Both sides vulnerable**

NORTH
♠ K Q 7
♡ A 8
♢ 10 2
♣ Q 7 6 5 4 2

WEST   EAST
♠ J 10 9 8   ♠ 6 4 3 2
♡ 9 5 2   ♡ K 7 6 4 3
♢ 6 5   ♢ 8 7 4 3
♣ K 10 9 8   ♣ None

SOUTH-D
♠ A 5
♡ Q J 10
♢ A K Q J 9
♣ A J 3

Defense Tricks:

☐ ☐ ☐ ☐ ☐ ☐ ☐ ☐ ☐ ☐ ☐ ☐

Bid the hand your way:

North	East	South	West
_____	_____	_____	_____
_____	_____	_____	_____
_____	_____	_____	_____
_____	_____	_____	_____

Opening Lead _____

112

How the hand was bid:

SOUTH	WEST	NORTH	EAST
2 NT	Pass	6 NT	All Pass
			Opening lead — ♠ J

How the hand was played: Declarer won the opening spade lead in dummy to lead a low club. If East followed suit, South could finesse and be sure of twelve tricks.

When East discarded a heart, South despondently finessed with the jack of clubs, losing to the king. Declarer had to try the heart finesse later and went down when this finesse failed.

South carefully pointed out that the odds were 20 to 1 against finding all the clubs in the West hand. Even then, he would make the contract if the heart finesse worked. The odds were about 40 to 1 against the fatal club break combined with a losing heart finesse.

It was sad but true. Still, South should make the contract by putting up the ace of clubs at the second trick instead of finessing.

CONTINUES WITH CLUB

South continues with a low club toward dummy. West dares not put up the king since then declarer can bring in the rest of the clubs and will have twelve tricks without the heart finesse.

When West plays a low club, declarer wins in dummy with the queen. He gets to his hand with a spade to try the heart finesse, not caring whether it wins or loses.

East can take the king of hearts, but then West doesn't get a club trick. South has enough tricks, with three spades, two hearts, five diamonds and two clubs.

Should You Trust Opponent's Bidding?

"My husband scolded me for failing to make this hand," writes a fan, "but I think he was just using hindsight. Please tell us who was right.

West dealer   **North-South vulnerable**

NORTH
♠ A Q 10 6 5
♡ K 3
◇ 7 5 4
♣ A 5 2

WEST-D
♠ K 8
♡ 8
◇ K Q J 9 3
♣ K Q 10 9 4

EAST
♠ J 9 7 4
♡ J 7 5 4
◇ 10 8 2
♣ J 6

SOUTH
♠ 3 2
♡ A Q 10 9 6 2
◇ A 6
♣ 8 7 3

Defense Tricks:

☐ ☐ ☐ ☐ ☐ ☐ ☐ ☐ ☐ ☐ ☐ ☐ ☐

Bid the hand your way:

North	East	South	West
_____	_____	_____	_____
_____	_____	_____	_____
_____	_____	_____	_____
_____	_____	_____	_____
		Opening Lead	_____

114

How the hand was bid:

WEST	NORTH	EAST	SOUTH
1 ◇	1 ♠	Pass	2 ♡
3 ♣	Pass	3 ◇	3 ♡
Pass	4 ♡	All Pass	

Opening lead — ◇ K

How the hand was played: "I took the first trick with the ace of diamonds and led a spade to win a finesse with dummy's queen. Then I took the king and ace of trumps, and the bad break beat me. I lost a trump, a diamond and two clubs.

"My husband said West was marked with ten cards in diamonds and clubs. When he showed up with two spades, he could hold only one heart, so I should have finessed through East for the jack of trumps.

"I don't trust West's bidding that much. He would bid just as much with only nine cards in his two suits and might hold J-8 of hearts instead of the singleton eight.

"If I lost a finesse to the doubleton jack of trumps, my husband would howl loud enough to be heard in Greenland. Are you going to back him up because he's a man, or are you going to be fair?"

FAIR IS FAIR

If it's put that way, I have to be fair. The lady is right: She should not trust West's bidding. Any girl whose husband can be heard in Greenland shouldn't trust an opponent.

But South should make her contract anyway. After taking the king and ace of trumps, she should lead a spade to the ace and ruff a spade. Back to dummy with a club and another spade ruff.

By this time, South has taken the first eight tricks and still has the Q-10 of trumps in her hand. She leads a club or a diamond and waits. Sooner or later she will get a trick with the ten of hearts as well as with the queen.

If pays to use the bidding to count an opponent's hand, but not if you can make absolutely sure of the count by playing the cards correctly. If you become known as a trusting player, nasty opponents will try to mislead you with unorthodox bids.

True Expert Carries Umbrella

The true bridge expert bids so aggressively that he may think of himself as a swashbuckler with a pistol in each hand and a cutlass between his teeth. In the play of the cards, however, he wears both belt and suspenders, and he carries an umbrella when there is nary a cloud in the sky.

South dealer   **Both sides vulnerable**

NORTH

♠ K 5 3 2
♡ K J 8
◇ A J 10 6 3
♣ 7

WEST   **EAST**

♠ 9 4   ♠ Q J 10 8
♡ 9 5 4 2   ♡ 10 7 3
◇ 8 7   ◇ K 9 4
♣ A 10 8 5 2   ♣ J 9 4

SOUTH-D

♠ A 7 6
♡ A Q 6
◇ Q 5 2
♣ K Q 6 3

Defense Tricks:

☐ ☐ ☐ ☐ ☐ ☐ ☐ ☐ ☐ ☐ ☐ ☐ ☐

Bid the hand your way:

North	East	South	West
_____	_____	_____	_____
_____	_____	_____	_____
_____	_____	_____	_____
_____	_____	_____	_____

Opening Lead _____

How the hand was bid:

SOUTH	WEST	NORTH	EAST
1 NT	Pass	2 ♣	Pass
2 ◊	Pass	3 ◊	Pass
3 NT	All Pass		

Opening lead — ♣ 5

How the hand was played: There's nothing fearfully daring about South's contract. South should bid game even if he doesn't know a swash from a buckle. The play is another story. South goes down if he forgets his umbrella.

West opens the five of clubs, and East plays the jack. The average declarer plays a cunning king to win this trick.

South must go after the diamonds, and East wins with the king and returns the nine of clubs. East continues with his remaining club to give West the rest of the suit.

The defenders collect one diamond and four clubs, defeating the contract. South takes the cutlasses out of his mouth to say ''Hard luck, partner!''

PESSIMISTIC PLAY

The expert sees that he can afford to lose three clubs but not four. He plays the hand with that distinction in mind. South must allow East to win the first trick with the jack of clubs. When East returns the nine of clubs, South must play low once more.

South plays one of his honors on the third round of clubs and is then safe. When East gets in with the king of diamonds, he has no club to lead. If East did have a club, the suit would then break 4-4, and South would lose only three club tricks anyway.

The pessimistic play gives up South's chance for two club tricks—except that South was never going to make a second club trick. The important thing is to limit West to three club tricks.

Use Bath Coup to Gain Time

"When you write about the trap known as the Bath Coup, what do you mean?" asks a reader. "Are you talking about a bathtub and the plumber's trap underneath the tub, or are you hinting that some bridge players are plumbers?"

South dealer   **North-South vulnerable**

NORTH
♠ 3
♡ K J 8 3
♢ A J 7 6 2
♣ A 6 5

WEST
♠ K J 10 7 6
♡ 9 4 2
♢ 8
♣ K Q 10 7

EAST
♠ Q 9 8 4 2
♡ 5
♢ Q 10 9 5
♣ 9 8 2

SOUTH-D
♠ A 5
♡ A Q 10 7 6
♢ K 4 3
♣ J 4 3

Defense Tricks:

☐ ☐ ☐ ☐ ☐ ☐ ☐ ☐ ☐ ☐ ☐ ☐ ☐

Bid the hand your way:

North	East	South	West
_____	_____	_____	_____
_____	_____	_____	_____
_____	_____	_____	_____
_____	_____	_____	_____

Opening Lead _____

118

How the hand was bid:

SOUTH	WEST	NORTH	EAST
1 ♡	1 ♠	3 ♡	3 ♠
Pass	4 ♠	5 ♡	All Pass

Opening lead — ♣ K

How the hand was played: What a nasty thought! I have made an agreement with the Plumbers' Union and the Butchers' Union not to mention them in this book, and I expect to keep my promise.

The Bath Coup, which has nothing to do with tubs, is named after the English resort town Bath, where the play developed a couple of hundred years ago in the days of whist. The Coup is even more useful at contract bridge.

Traditionally, the Bath Coup is a refusal to win the opening lead of the king when declarer holds A-J-x of the suit. If the opener falls into the trap of continuing, declarer wins with the jack. If the opener is clever enough to switch to a different suit, declarer gains time and may find a way to get rid of his loser in the suit.

DIFFERENT POSITION

The Bath Coup may be executed with the ace and jack in different hands. In this case, for example, South refuses to win the first club trick.

West is forced to switch, probably to a spade. South wins, draws trumps, cashes the king of diamonds and gives up a diamond to East.

East returns a club to dummy's ace, but it is too late. Declarer cashes the ace of diamonds, ruffs a diamond and ruffs a spade in dummy. He can then discard his last club on dummy's last diamond to make the contract.

South goes down if he takes the first club trick with dummy's ace. East wins an early diamond trick and returns a club, whereupon West takes two club tricks.

Playing Hand Well Beats Complaining

One of the advantages of living in a free country is that you can bid your hand as you please. If an opponent doesn't like your bidding you can tell him to go climb a tree. (Players who can't climb shouldn't complain about an opponent's bidding.)

North dealer   **East-West vulnerable**

NORTH-D
- ♠ K Q
- ♡ Q
- ◇ A 10 7 6 5
- ♣ K J 9 6 5

WEST	EAST
♠ A J 8 7 6 5 3 2	♠ 9
♡ 7	♡ J 10 9 8 6 3
◇ 9 4 3	◇ K Q J 2
♣ 2	♣ A 3

SOUTH
- ♠ 10 4
- ♡ A K 5 4 2
- ◇ 8
- ♣ Q 10 8 7 4

Defense Tricks:

☐ ☐ ☐ ☐ ☐ ☐ ☐ ☐ ☐ ☐ ☐ ☐ ☐

Bid the hand your way:

North	East	South	West
_____	_____	_____	_____
_____	_____	_____	_____
_____	_____	_____	_____
_____	_____	_____	_____
		Opening Lead	_____

How the hand was bid:

NORTH	EAST	SOUTH	WEST
1 ♦	1 ♥	Double	1 ♠
Pass	Pass	2 ♣	Pass
3 ♣	Pass	4 ♣	Pass
5 ♣	All Pass		

Opening lead — ♥ 7

How the hand was played: Declarer won the first trick with dummy's queen of hearts. There wasn't a thing to worry about, he decided, as he led a trump from dummy.

East stepped up with the ace of clubs and shot back his singleton spade. West took the ace of spades and returned a spade, whereupon East's ruff defeated the contract.

South was overwhelmed by West's timidity. "Eight spades in his hand," South complained, "and he got up enough nerve to bid one spade. Whoever taught him to bid was taking money under false pretenses. Why, I have a five-week-old puppy that would bid four spades on that hand!"

It's true that West could make four spades, but South could make five clubs by playing the hand well. What's more, South could score more for making his contract than for proving that West hadn't bid enough.

SHOULD DISCARD SPADE

South should meet the only threat by discarding a spade from dummy. At the second trick, declarer cashes the ace of diamonds, then ruffs a diamond to lead the ace of hearts.

West ruffs, and dummy overruffs. Declarer ruffs another diamond and leads the king of hearts. If West can ruff again, dummy can overruff and there will be no further threat with the removal of the last low trump.

Actually, West cannot ruff the king of hearts. Declarer discards a spade from dummy, and the hand is over. The defenders can get their two black aces but nothing else.

Ruff Loser with Worthless Trump

You can often profit by ruffing a loser with an otherwise worthless trump. If you need a ruffing trick, play the trumps in such a way that you don't have to ruff with a trump needed for some other purpose.

South dealer   **North-South vulnerable**

NORTH
♠ A Q 7 6 2
♡ Q 10 3
♢ A Q 4
♣ 4 3

WEST   EAST
♠ 10 9 8 4   ♠ K J 5
♡ 8 7 5 2   ♡ K J 9 6 4
♢ J 10 9   ♢ 2
♣ A 9   ♣ J 10 8 6

SOUTH-D
♠ 3
♡ A
♢ K 8 7 6 5 3
♣ K Q 7 5 2

Defense Tricks:

☐ ☐ ☐ ☐ ☐ ☐ ☐ ☐ ☐ ☐ ☐ ☐ ☐ ☐

Bid the hand your way:

North	East	South	West
_____	_____	_____	_____
_____	_____	_____	_____
_____	_____	_____	_____
		Opening Lead _____	

How the hand was bid:

SOUTH	WEST	NORTH	EAST
1 ◊	Pass	1 ♠	Pass
2 ♣	Pass	3 NT	Pass
4 ♣	Pass	4 ◊	Pass
5 ◊	All Pass		

Opening lead — ◊ J

How the hand was played: When West opens the jack of diamonds, declarer must win the trick in dummy with the ace or queen. South will have to ruff a club eventually, and he wants to save dummy's low trump for that purpose.

At the second trick, declarer leads a club from dummy, losing the king to West's ace. Back comes a trump, and declarer must make sure of winning this trick also in dummy. If South won in his own hand, he would have to ruff a club with dummy's high trump, and this would set up a trump trick for West.

South continues with a club to the queen and a low club toward dummy. This gives West a chance to step up with the nine of diamonds and thus win a trump trick, but South is still sure of his contract.

CAN RUFF LATER

When West ruffs high, declarer discards a spade from the dummy and saves the trump for a later ruff. No matter what West returns, South can get to his hand with the ace of hearts and lead another low club to ruff in dummy. The last club is then good, and South is home.

South would lose the contract if he drew West's last trump. He would then have to lose two more club tricks. In effect, West ruffs a trick that his partner would win.

Still, West cannot gain by refusing to ruff the third round of clubs. If he does, declarer ruffs the club in dummy, gets to his hand with the ace of hearts and then draws the last trump with the king.

Don't Run When Race Is Lost

There is something to be said for the dogged spirit that keeps you running when the race is clearly lost. The word to be said is "Phooey!" Be a gracious winner, not a dogged loser.

South dealer   **North-South vulnerable**

NORTH
♠ Q 9 2
♡ K 4 2
◇ K 5
♣ K 10 9 6 3

WEST   **EAST**
♠ 7 6 5   ♠ 4 3
♡ Q 10 7   ♡ J 9 8 6
◇ Q 10 9   ◇ A J 8 3
♣ Q J 7 5   ♣ 8 4 2

SOUTH-D
♠ A K J 10 8
♡ A 5 3
◇ 7 6 4 2
♣ A

Defense Tricks:

☐ ☐ ☐ ☐ ☐ ☐ ☐ ☐ ☐ ☐ ☐ ☐ ☐

Bid the hand your way:

North	East	South	West
_____	_____	_____	_____
_____	_____	_____	_____
_____	_____	_____	_____
_____	_____	_____	_____

Opening Lead _____

124

How the hand was bid:

SOUTH	WEST	NORTH	EAST
1 ♠	Pass	2 ♣	Pass
2 ♠	Pass	3 ♠	Pass
4 ♠	All Pass		

Opening lead — ♠ 7

How the hand was played: West opened a trump, and South won. He returned a diamond, losing dummy's king to the ace. Back came a trump.

It was now clear that South could not win the race to ruff a diamond in the dummy. In fact this was clear at the first trick. But South led another diamond anyway; maybe the opponents would slip.

The opponents had no intention of slipping. West won the second diamond and returned a third round of trumps to take the last trump out of dummy.

South eventually discarded his losing heart on dummy's king of clubs, but he had to lose four diamonds. Down one.

SECOND PLAN

After winning the first round of trumps in his hand, South should immediately cash the ace of clubs. Then, and only then, is it time to lead diamonds.

East captures the king of diamonds with the ace and returns a trump to dummy's nine. (Naturally, South won the first trick with the ten.) South discards a heart on the king of clubs and ruffs a club with the king of spades.

Now South leads another diamond. Back comes a trump to dummy's queen. The race to ruff a diamond is lost, but South's other plan is working. He ruffs another club, thus setting up dummy's last club. He gets to dummy with the king of hearts to cash the last club, thus making his tenth trick.

Don't Sacrifice against Poor Player

The most productive bid doesn't always depend on the cards you hold or the skill of your partner. You must also consider the bridge ability of your opponents.

West dealer   **Both sides vulnerable**

NORTH
♠ 5 3 2
♡ None
♢ A K Q J 4 3
♣ 8 4 3 2

WEST-D   EAST
♠ 6   ♠ J 10 9 8
♡ A K Q 6 5 3   ♡ 10 9 8 4
♢ 9 2   ♢ 8 5
♣ A 9 7 5   ♣ Q J 10

SOUTH
♠ A K Q 7 4
♡ J 7 2
♢ 10 7 6
♣ K 6

Defense Tricks:

☐ ☐ ☐ ☐ ☐ ☐ ☐ ☐ ☐ ☐ ☐ ☐

Bid the hand your way:

North	East	South	West
_____	_____	_____	_____
_____	_____	_____	_____
_____	_____	_____	_____
_____		_____	_____

Opening Lead _____

How the hand was bid:

WEST	NORTH	EAST	SOUTH
1 ♡	2 ◇	Pass	2 ♠
3 ♡	3 ♠	Pass	4 ♠
All Pass			

Opening lead — ♡ K

How the hand was played: East came close to bidding two hearts at his first turn and even closer to bidding four hearts later. He decided not to encourage a sacrifice bid of five hearts because South was an inexperienced player.

East's timid bidding paid off when South found a way to go down at four spades. Declarer ruffed the opening heart lead in dummy and then began to draw trumps with the ace and king. When the trumps failed to break, South was down two for a penalty of 200 points.

Against a more reliable declarer, East would have raised hearts at some stage. West would probably be doubled at five hearts, thus losing 200 points instead of making a profit.

SHOULD MAKE GAME

South should, of course, make the game and rubber by a more careful line of play. After ruffing the first heart in dummy, declarer should play a low trump from each hand.

This allows East to win, and the switch to clubs would give the defenders two more tricks. The defense would end there, however, No matter what is led, South can win, draw trumps with the A-K-Q and then run the diamonds.

A sacrifice bid is useful only when it costs very little and when the opponents would have made their contract. Avoid sacrificing against an unskillful player.

Suicidal Mania Can Be Avoided

Bridge players sometimes marvel at the lemming, the strange Scandinavian rodent that cannot be prevented from committing suicide in the sea. It is less well known that the lemming marvels at bridge players, many of whom cannot be prevented from doing themselves in at the bridge table.

South dealer   **North-South vulnerable**

NORTH
♠ A 8 6 3
♡ 9 8 2
♢ K 8
♣ 9 7 3 2

WEST   EAST
♠ K Q J 10 7   ♠ 9 5 2
♡ A J 10   ♡ 7 6 5 4
♢ Q 10 7 5   ♢ J 9 2
♣ 10   ♣ J 8 6

SOUTH-D
♠ 4
♡ K Q 3
♢ A 6 4 3
♣ A K Q 5 4

Defense Tricks:

☐ ☐ ☐ ☐ ☐ ☐ ☐ ☐ ☐ ☐ ☐

Bid the hand your way:

North	East	South	West
_____	_____	_____	_____
_____	_____	_____	_____
_____	_____	_____	_____
_____	_____	_____	_____
		Opening Lead _____	

How the hand was bid:

SOUTH	WEST	NORTH	EAST
1 ♣	1 ♠	2 ♣	Pass
2 ♦	2 ♠	Pass	Pass
4 ♣	Pass	5 ♣	All Pass

Opening lead — ♠ K

How the hand was played: South took the ace of spades, drew two rounds of trumps, cashed the top diamonds and ruffed a diamond in dummy. He got back by ruffing a spade and tried to ruff his last diamond in dummy.

Naturally, East overruffed. The defenders eventually got two heart tricks, and South met a lemming's end.

Declarer made the right move when he took the first trick in dummy with the ace of spades. He didn't make one good move after that.

At the second trick, declarer should lead a heart, using the king to force out the ace. West returns a spade, and South ruffs.

DRAWS TRUMPS

South can then afford to draw two rounds of trumps. He takes the top diamonds, ruffs a diamond in dummy and get to his hand with the queen of hearts. Then South leads his last diamond.

When West follows with the queen of diamonds, South knows that East is out of diamonds and that East has a trump higher than dummy. To ruff in dummy is a lemming's trick: Nobody can admire it except another lemming.

Instead, South should discard dummy's last heart, allowing West to win the diamond trick. No matter what West returns, South will be able to ruff his last heart in dummy. East cannot overruff because he must follow suit.

It Pays You to Know Your Friends

One of the pleasant features of some bridge hands is that you can afford to give away a trick or two. Make sure that you give them to your friends rather than to your enemies.

South dealer   **Both sides vulnerable**

NORTH
- ♠ K J 2
- ♡ 10 4
- ◇ K 7 3
- ♣ K Q J 5 4

WEST
- ♠ Q 7 5 3
- ♡ Q 9 7 3
- ◇ Q 9 8
- ♣ 10 7

EAST
- ♠ 6
- ♡ K 8 6 5
- ◇ A J 10 6 2
- ♣ 9 8 6

SOUTH-D
- ♠ A 10 9 8 4
- ♡ A J 2
- ◇ 5 4
- ♣ A 3 2

Defense Tricks:

☐ ☐ ☐ ☐ ☐ ☐ ☐ ☐ ☐ ☐ ☐ ☐

Bid the hand your way:

North	East	South	West
———	———	———	———
———	———	———	———
———	———	———	———
———	———	———	———

Opening Lead _____

How the hand was bid:

SOUTH	WEST	NORTH	EAST
1 ♠	Pass	2 ♣	Pass
2 ♠	Pass	4 ♠	All Pass

Opening lead — ♡ 3

How the hand was played: East put up the king of hearts at the first trick, and South won with the ace—a mistake. He led a trump to dummy's king, another mistake, and returned the jack of spades.

East discarded the six of diamonds, and South played low for lack of anything better to do. West won with the queen of spades and shifted to the eight of diamonds in response to his partner's signal.

In desperation, South put up dummy's king of diamonds. East took the ace and jack of diamonds and then switched back to hearts to defeat the contract.

BAD PLAY

South played the hearts and spades badly since he gave a trick in each suit to his enemy. If East is allowed to win a heart and a spade, he cannot get two diamond tricks. As we have seen, West could and did produce two diamond tricks by leading through dummy's king.

South should refuse the first heart trick, win the second and lead the ten of spades for a finesse. If this happens to lose, the defenders can get only one heart, one spade and one diamond.

As the cards lie, however, the ten of spades would win. South continues with a spade to dummy's jack, the king of spades and then gets to his hand with the ace of clubs to draw the last trump. The rest of the clubs then bring in eleven tricks instead of only nine.

Correct Equipment for Perfect Player

If you want to be the perfect bridge player, you must keep a false beard in your pocket. After you have made the perfect play, you can whip out the beard and look innocent.

South dealer   **North-South vulnerable**

NORTH
- ♠ K 10 3 2
- ♡ Q 6 4
- ◊ K 10 5
- ♣ 9 4 3

WEST
- ♠ 8 5
- ♡ K J 9 2
- ◊ Q J 9 4
- ♣ Q 8 6

EAST
- ♠ 9 6
- ♡ A 8 7 3
- ◊ 8 7 2
- ♣ 10 7 5 2

SOUTH-D
- ♠ A Q J 7 4
- ♡ 10 5
- ◊ A 6 3
- ♣ A K J

Defense Tricks:

☐ ☐ ☐ ☐ ☐ ☐ ☐ ☐ ☐ ☐ ☐ ☐

Bid the hand your way:

North	East	South	West
_____	_____	_____	_____
_____	_____	_____	_____
_____	_____	_____	_____
_____	_____	_____	_____
		Opening Lead _____	

How the hand was bid:

SOUTH	WEST	NORTH	EAST
1 ♠	Pass	2 ♠	Pass
4 ♠	All Pass		

Opening lead — ♠ 5

How the hand was played: West opened a trump but didn't know anything about beards. South looked at West, saw that he was still the same person who had led the trump and realized what was going on.

Any opening lead but trump would have given South his contract. If West led a low heart, declarer would play low from dummy and would eventually develop a trick with dummy's queen. If West opened the queen of diamonds, South would take the ace and later win a finesse with dummy's ten. And if West opened a club, South would get a free finesse.

The trump lead gave South a chance to go down, and South would do just that if he tried to make the contract by his own efforts. Instead, South worked out the reason for West's opening lead and proceeded on the assumption that West held strength in each side suit.

FORCES LEAD

Declarer won the trump in his hand and led a heart, losing dummy's queen to the ace. Back came a club, and South stepped up with the ace. Back came a club, and South stepped up with the ace. South gave up another heart and ruffed the heart return.

Now South drew a second round of trumps, cashed the top diamonds and gave up a diamond. West had to win and had to give up the trick that his opening lead had saved. If West led a club, South would get the free finesse, and if West led anything else, dummy would ruff while South got rid of the jack of clubs.

All for lack of a beard.

Reporter Makes the News

The average player likes nothing better than to watch the experts making mistakes. This may account for the perennial popularity of "Championship Bridge" on television. Sometimes the experts play like champions, of course, as in this case.

South dealer   **North-South vulnerable**

```
                    NORTH
                    ♠ 7 4 3
                    ♡ K J 9 8 3
                    ◇ A 7
                    ♣ A 6 3
     WEST                          EAST
     ♠ A Q J 8 5                   ♠ 10 9
     ♡ 6 5 2                       ♡ 4
     ◇ Q J 10                      ◇ 9 8 4 3 2
     ♣ 10 7                        ♣ Q J 9 8 4
                    SOUTH-D
                    ♠ K 6 2
                    ♡ A Q 10 7
                    ◇ K 6 5
                    ♣ K 5 2
```

Defense Tricks:

☐ ☐ ☐ ☐ ☐ ☐ ☐ ☐ ☐ ☐ ☐ ☐

Bid the hand your way:

North	East	South	West
‾‾‾‾	‾‾‾‾	‾‾‾‾	‾‾‾‾
‾‾‾‾	‾‾‾‾	‾‾‾‾	‾‾‾‾
‾‾‾‾	‾‾‾‾	‾‾‾‾	‾‾‾‾
‾‾‾‾	‾‾‾‾	‾‾‾‾	‾‾‾‾
		Opening Lead ‾‾‾‾	

How the hand was bid:

SOUTH	WEST	NORTH	EAST
1 ♡	1 ♠	3 ♡	Pass
3 NT	Pass	4 ♡	All Pass

Opening lead — ◊ Q

How the hand was played: Declarer was the late Albert H. Morehead, who covered the bridge beat for *The New York Times* for 26 years. Throughout his long career, Morehead preserved the habit of playing the right card at the right time.

In this hand, Morehead took the ace of diamonds, drew three rounds of trumps, cashed the king of diamonds and ruffed a diamond in dummy. By this time, he knew that West had started with six red cards and, presumably, at least five spades for his spade overcall. West couldn't have more than two clubs, and East couldn't have more than two spades.

TRICK GETS LOST

Morehead saw a way to sweep a trick under the carpet, where it would get lost. He cashed the king and ace of clubs and led a spade from dummy, playing the king from his hand.

West took the ace of spades but could not collect the four tricks that seemed to belong to the defense. If West continued with the queen of spades, he could get a third spade trick but would then have to lead a fourth spade, allowing declarer to ruff in dummy and discard the losing club from his hand.

If West led a low spade after taking the ace, East could win the trick and cash a club, but then East would be out of spades. East would have to lead either a club or a diamond—and dummy would ruff while South discarded his losing spade.

Read Defense to Make Slam

When your partner has made the opening lead, you know just which card to lead when returning his suit. Apply this knowledge when you are the declarer.

North dealer   **Both sides vulnerable**

NORTH-D

♠ 8 7 5 3
♡ A K 9 4
♢ A
♣ K Q 7 3

WEST	EAST
♠ 9 6 2	♠ J 4
♡ 10 5	♡ Q J 8 7 3
♢ J 9 7 4	♢ 10 8 5 2
♣ J 10 9 4	♣ A 8

SOUTH

♠ A K Q 10
♡ 6 2
♢ K Q 6 3
♣ 6 5 2

Defense Tricks:

☐ ☐ ☐ ☐ ☐ ☐ ☐ ☐ ☐ ☐ ☐ ☐ ☐

Bid the hand your way:

North	East	South	West
___	___	___	___
___	___	___	___
___	___	___	___
		___	___

Opening Lead _____

136

How the hand was bid:

NORTH	EAST	SOUTH	WEST
1 ♣	Pass	1 ♠	Pass
3 ♠	Pass	4 ◇	Pass
4 ♡	Pass	4 NT	Pass
5 ♡	Pass	6 ♠	All Pass

Opening lead — ♣ J

How the hand was played: West led the jack of clubs, and dummy's queen lost to the ace. East returned the eight of clubs, driving out the king. Declarer cashed the ace of diamonds, drew two rounds of trumps and discarded dummy's low clubs on high diamonds. So far, so good.

South had to ruff a club and a diamond in dummy but went wrong by ruffing the club first. He cashed dummy's top hearts and got back by ruffing a heart—but West discarded a diamond on this trick. When South next led a diamond, West ruffed with the nine of spades to defeat the contract.

EARLY CLUE

The clue to the right play was in the first two tricks. East returned the eight of clubs, showing that he didn't hold the nine. West's opening lead of the jack of clubs showed the ten. These plays accounted for all the clubs.

South knew that West had started with four clubs and three trumps. The hand could be made only if West also held two hearts and four diamonds. Even with the ideal distribution, South could make his slam only by ruffing the losing diamond before the club.

West would follow suit on the fourth round of diamonds, and dummy would ruff. When declarer then cashed the top hearts and ruffed a heart, West could discard a club—but this would do no harm since West still had two clubs. South would ruff his last club safely and take the last trick with his high trump, making the slam.

Don't Waste Trump for Finesse

The easiest way to take a diamond finesse is to lead a diamond. A more devious way, possible only if diamonds are trumps, is to lead a side suit when you are ready to overruff the opponent. This devious way may help you keep one trump for other purposes.

South dealer   **Both sides vulnerable**

NORTH
♠ A J 6 5 2
♡ K 4
◇ 8 7 5 3
♣ K 6

WEST   EAST
♠ 10 8 7 3   ♠ 9 4
♡ Q J 10 9 3   ♡ A 8 7 6 2
◇ None   ◇ J 9 6 4
♣ J 9 5 3   ♣ Q 10

SOUTH-D
♠ K Q
♡ 5
◇ A K Q 10 2
♣ A 8 7 4 2

Defense Tricks:

☐ ☐ ☐ ☐ ☐ ☐ ☐ ☐ ☐ ☐ ☐ ☐ ☐

Bid the hand your way:

North	East	South	West
_____	_____	_____	_____
_____	_____	_____	_____
_____	_____	_____	_____
_____	_____	_____	_____

Opening Lead _____

How the hand was bid:

SOUTH	WEST	NORTH	EAST
1 ◊	Pass	1 ♠	Pass
2 ♣	Pass	3 ◊	Pass
4 ♣	Pass	4 ♠	Pass
6 ◊	All Pass		

Opening lead — ♡Q

How the hand was played: South ruffs the second round of hearts and leads the ace of diamonds, expecting an easy time. West discards a heart, and South must revise his expectations.

South must finesse to draw East's trumps, but he will wind up in the garbage can if he uses one of dummy's trumps for the finesse.

Suppose South leads a club to dummy's king and returns a trump. Declarer can win a finesse with the ten of diamonds and can then draw the rest of the trumps. But then dummy is out of trumps and neither the spades nor the clubs can be run. South must give up at least one trick.

CASH SPADES

South makes the contract easily by cashing the king and queen of spades before leading a club to dummy's king. Then he leads the ace of spades from dummy.

East cannot stay out of trouble by failing to ruff. Declarer can then lead three good spades from dummy and discard three low clubs from his hand. He will still be in dummy so can lead a trump for the finesse. South draws all of the trumps and takes the last trick with the ace of clubs.

If East ruffs a spade, South overruffs. This is a sort of finesse, and South draws the rest of the trumps. The vital difference is that one trump is still left in dummy. South cashes the ace of clubs and ruffs a club, after which dummy wins the rest of the tricks with any spades that are still left.

Virtue May Handicap Players

If you belong to the Older Generation, you may be too virtuous for your own good. Our children, taught to use things up as quickly as possible, would have less trouble with this hand than the oldster who played it.

North dealer   **Neither side vulnerable**

NORTH-D
- ♠ A K 10
- ♡ A K 4
- ◊ 4
- ♣ K Q 10 9 5 2

WEST
- ♠ 5 2
- ♡ J 9 2
- ◊ Q J 10 8
- ♣ A J 8 4

EAST
- ♠ Q 6 3
- ♡ 8 3
- ◊ K 9 6 5 2
- ♣ 7 6 3

SOUTH
- ♠ J 9 8 7 4
- ♡ Q 10 7 6 5
- ◊ A 7 3
- ♣ None

Defense Tricks:

☐ ☐ ☐ ☐ ☐ ☐ ☐ ☐ ☐ ☐ ☐ ☐ ☐ ☐

Bid the hand your way:

North	East	South	West
_____	_____	_____	_____
_____	_____	_____	_____
_____	_____	_____	_____
_____	_____	_____	_____

Opening Lead _____

How the hand was bid:

NORTH	EAST	SOUTH	WEST
1 ♣	Pass	1 ♠	Pass
3 ♣	Pass	3 ♡	Pass
3 ♠	Pass	4 ◊	Pass
4 NT	Pass	5 ◊	Pass
6 ♠	All Pass		

Opening lead — ◊ Q

How the hand was played: South took the ace of diamonds and ruffed a diamond with dummy's ten of trumps. This economical play was his undoing.

Declarer got to his hand by ruffing a club and ruffed another diamond with the king of trumps. Then he cashed the ace of trumps and ruffed another club.

When South led the jack of spades, East won and returned a club. This made South use up his last trump and left East with the thirteenth trump and control of the hand. South was down three—all because he had been taught the value of thrift.

NO TROUBLE

A youngster would have no trouble with the hand because he would rush to use up his high cards. The young South takes the ace of diamonds and ruffs a diamond with dummy's ace of trumps instead of the ten.

Declarer gets to his hand by ruffing a club and ruffs another diamond with the king of trumps. Then he leads the ten of trumps from dummy and overtakes with the jack, still following the principle of using up his high cards.

South leads the nine of spades to force out the queen, and East returns a club to make declarer ruff. The difference is that South has a trump and can draw East's last trump.

South is now in position to run the hearts. He makes his slam contract—all because he has been taught to use things up instead of saving them.

141

Name Doesn't Matter If You Make Play

Thirty years ago Ely Culbertson dramatically called a certain bridge play "The Coup Without a Name." Modern writers prefer to call it "The Scissors Coup" because it cuts communications between the two opponents. Call it what you like, as long as you make the play when it is needed.

West dealer   **East-West vulnerable**

NORTH
♠ 4 3
♡ K J 6 5 2
◇ K Q J
♣ 6 4 2

WEST-D   EAST
♠ A 8 7 5   ♠ None
♡ A 7 4 3   ♡ Q 10 9 8
◇ 6   ◇ 8 7 5 4 2
♣ K Q J 10   ♣ A 9 8 5

SOUTH
♠ K Q J 10 9 6 2
♡ None
◇ A 10 9 3
♣ 7 3

Defense Tricks:

☐ ☐ ☐ ☐ ☐ ☐ ☐ ☐ ☐ ☐ ☐ ☐

Bid the hand your way:

North	East	South	West
_____	_____	_____	_____
_____	_____	_____	_____
_____	_____	_____	_____
_____	_____	_____	_____
		Opening Lead	_____

How the hand was bid:

WEST	NORTH	EAST	SOUTH
1 ♣	1 ♡	2 ♣	4 ♠
Double	All Pass		

Opening lead — ♣ K

How the hand was played: West opens the king of clubs, and East signals with the nine. West shrewdly decides against leading another club. Instead, he shifts to his singleton diamond.

If declarer returns a trump, West takes the ace of trumps and leads the ten of clubs to East's ace. East then returns a diamond, and West's ruff defeats the contract.

This pretty defense gives great joy to all except two players at the table. Still, South should make his contract in spite of the clever shift to diamonds.

CUTS COMMUNICATIONS

South must cut communications between East and West. If East never gains the lead, he can never give his partner a diamond ruff.

Upon winning the second trick in dummy with the king of diamonds, South must not lead trumps. Instead, declarer leads the king of hearts from dummy. South throws away a club instead of ruffing, and West must win the trick.

This maneuver gives West a trick with the ace of hearts but prevents East from getting a trick with the ace of clubs. It is better than an even exchange for South because East never gets the lead—which means that West never gets his diamond ruff.

After executing this little coup, South can easily draw trumps and run his diamonds in safety.

Rely on Your Head Instead of on Luck

There are bridge players for whom finesses always succeed and suits always break favorably. Since we don't belong to this fortunate group, we must use our heads to make up the difference.

South dealer   **Both sides vulnerable**

NORTH
♠ Q 9 2
♡ A 7 6 5 2
♢ 7 3 2
♣ Q 6

WEST   **EAST**
♠ 6 5 3   ♠ 4
♡ K J 10 9   ♡ Q 8
♢ Q J 10   ♢ 9 8 5 4
♣ 10 9 5   ♣ J 8 7 4 3 2

SOUTH-D
♠ A K J 10 8 7
♡ 4 3
♢ A K 6
♣ A K

Defense Tricks:

☐ ☐ ☐ ☐ ☐ ☐ ☐ ☐ ☐ ☐ ☐ ☐ ☐ ☐

Bid the hand your way:

North	East	South	West
_____	_____	_____	_____
_____	_____	_____	_____
_____	_____	_____	_____

Opening Lead _____

How the hand was bid:

SOUTH	WEST	NORTH	EAST
2 ♠	Pass	3 ♠	Pass
4 ◇	Pass	4 ♡	Pass
4 NT	Pass	5 ◇	Pass
5 NT	Pass	6 ♣	Pass
6 ♠	All Pass		

Opening lead — ◇ Q

How the hand was played: South took the king of diamonds, led a heart to dummy's ace and gave up a heart. There was nothing wrong with this line of play if South happened to be wearing the right horseshoe around his neck.

West took the second heart and returned another diamond. South won, cashed the ace of spades and led a trump to dummy's nine. Then he ruffed a heart, discovering that the six missing hearts had not broken 3-3.

This was very sad. There was no way to set up the long heart and also cash it. Sooner or later, South had to give up a diamond trick and was therefore down one.

SIMPLE PLAY

A very simple play would bring the slam home. At the second trick, South should give up a heart trick instead of taking dummy's ace of hearts.

The defenders return a diamond to South's ace. South cashes the ace of trumps, leads a heart to dummy's ace and ruffs a heart. Declarer then leads a trump to dummy's nine and ruffs another heart.

By this time, dummy's last heart is good. South leads a trump to dummy's queen and cashes the last heart, pitching away the losing diamond.

The advantage of losing the first heart instead of the second is that South gets to dummy with the ace of hearts in time to do something useful—he can ruff a heart.

Match Bold Bidding with Cautious Play

If you don't mind mixed metaphors, the secret of winning at bridge is to bid a hand to the hilt and then play the pants off the cards. No European expert is more famous for both of these arts than Mrs. Rixi Markus, for many years one of Great Britain's most distinguished players.

South dealer   **Both sides vulnerable**

NORTH
- ♠ A K 7
- ♡ J 4
- ◊ A K 10 9 8 5
- ♣ 9 8

WEST
- ♠ 9 8 4 3
- ♡ K 9 5
- ◊ Q 7 4
- ♣ Q 3 2

EAST
- ♠ J 10 5
- ♡ 10 7 6 2
- ◊ J 6 3 2
- ♣ 6 5

SOUTH-D
- ♠ Q 6 2
- ♡ A Q 8 3
- ◊ None
- ♣ A K J 10 7 4

Defense Tricks:

☐ ☐ ☐ ☐ ☐ ☐ ☐ ☐ ☐ ☐ ☐ ☐ ☐

Bid the hand your way:

North	East	South	West
_____	_____	_____	_____
_____	_____	_____	_____
_____	_____	_____	_____
_____	_____	_____	_____
		Opening Lead _____	

146

How the hand was bid:

SOUTH	WEST	NORTH	EAST
1 ♣	Pass	1 ♦	Pass
1 ♡	Pass	3 NT	Pass
6 ♣	All Pass		

Opening lead — ♠ 3

How the hand was played: Mrs. Markus leaped to six clubs to keep the bidding simple. Making the slam was not quite so simple.

It would be easy to try the trump finesse first and the heart finesse later, relying on one of the finesses to work. When both fail, the slam is down, but at least you have a reasonable excuse to give to your partner.

Since Mrs. Markus is just as cautious in the play as she is bold in the bidding, she found a way to make the slam without risking either finesse.

The English expert took the first trick in dummy with the ace of spades, discarded two hearts on the top diamonds and ruffed a diamond with the ten of clubs.

HIDDEN ENTRY

The next step was to lead the four of clubs from the South hand. West stepped up with the queen of clubs and returned a spade to the queen.

Mrs. Markus led the seven of clubs to dummy's nine, thus finding a hidden entry to dummy. This put her in position to ruff a diamond with the jack of clubs.

With the diamonds thus established, Mrs. Markus drew the last trump with the king of clubs and got to dummy with the king of spades to discard the queen of hearts on a good diamond.

When you play the cards like this, you can afford to be a frisky bidder.

Don't Get Headaches When You Can Signal

One way to influence your partner is to think with great concentration about the suits you want him to lead. If you have enough telepathic power and if the wind is blowing from the right direction, your partner may get the message.

South dealer   **Both sides vulnerable**

NORTH
♠ K 6 4
♡ 8 5 2
♢ A Q 9 7 3
♣ J 3

WEST   EAST
♠ A 2   ♠ 9 7 5 3
♡ Q J 10 7 4 3   ♡ A 9
♢ 6 4   ♢ K 8 2
♣ 7 5 2   ♣ 10 9 8 6

SOUTH-D
♠ Q J 10 8
♡ K 6
♢ J 10 5
♣ A K Q 4

Defense Tricks:

☐ ☐ ☐ ☐ ☐ ☐ ☐ ☐ ☐ ☐ ☐ ☐

Bid the hand your way:

North	East	South	West
＿＿＿	＿＿＿	＿＿＿	＿＿＿
＿＿＿	＿＿＿	＿＿＿	＿＿＿
＿＿＿	＿＿＿	＿＿＿	＿＿＿
＿＿＿	＿＿＿	＿＿＿	＿＿＿

Opening Lead ＿＿＿

How the hand was bid:

SOUTH	WEST	NORTH	EAST
1 NT	Pass	3 NT	All Pass

Opening lead — ♡ Q

How the hand was played: West led the queen of hearts, and East took the ace and returned the nine of hearts to declarer's king. South promptly took the diamond finesse, losing to the king.

East considered his return for quite a while, and West thought so hard about spades that he got a headache. West didn't feel any better when his partner eventually returned a club to dummy's weakness.

South rattled off four clubs and four diamonds, making game and rubber. West then took the rest with the ace of spades and good hearts.

WRONG ALLEY

If you blame West's faulty concentration for this unfortunate result, you're barking up the wrong alley. West had his chance at the second trick to show that his entry was in spades rather than in clubs.

When South won the second trick with the king of hearts, West should drop the jack of hearts. This unnecessarily high card shows that West's entry is in a high suit (spades), not a low suit (clubs).

This is an illustration of the Suit Preference Signal. When you are not trying to win a trick or to signal ordinary encouragement or discouragement, you can play an unnecessarily high or low card to show the location of your side strength. A high card shows strength in a high suit, and a low card shows strength in a low suit.

Tired Player Is Difficult Partner

It's perfectly possible to play bridge when you're too tired to plan the play of a hand. Just don't expect your partners to be delirious with joy. This hand was played by a very tired businessman.

East dealer   **Both sides vulnerable**

NORTH
♠ J 10 3
♡ 7
♢ A J 10 4
♣ J 7 6 4 2

WEST   EAST-D
♠ 7 4   ♠ 9 6 2
♡ 6 5 2   ♡ A K J 10 9 4
♢ 8 5 3 2   ♢ K 9 7
♣ A 10 8 3   ♣ Q

SOUTH
♠ A K Q 8 5
♡ Q 8 3
♢ Q 6
♣ K 9 5

Defense Tricks:

☐ ☐ ☐ ☐ ☐ ☐ ☐ ☐ ☐ ☐ ☐ ☐

Bid the hand your way:

North	East	South	West
_____	_____	_____	_____
_____	_____	_____	_____
_____	_____	_____	_____
_____	_____	_____	
		Opening Lead	_____

150

EAST	SOUTH	WEST	NORTH
1 ♡	Double	Pass	2 ♣
2 ♡	2 ♠	Pass	4 ♠
All Pass			

Opening lead — ♡ 6

How the hand was played: East took the king of hearts and shifted to the queen of clubs. South covered with the king, losing to the ace. Back came a low club, and South wisely played low from dummy. East ruffed and returned a trump.

South won the trump, ruffed a heart in dummy and got back with a trump. He studied the dummy for a moment or two, then shrugged his shoulders and led the queen of diamonds for a finesse.

East took the king of diamonds and the ace of hearts, collecting 200 points. South looked tired, and North looked daggers.

POSTPONE RUFF

When East returns the trump, South should not be in a hurry to ruff a heart in dummy. He should draw two trumps, followed by a club to the jack and a club ruff.

South leads a diamond to dummy's ace, discards the queen of diamonds on dummy's last club and leads the jack of diamonds through East. The opening bid clearly locates the king of diamonds in the East hand.

East puts up the king of diamonds, and South ruffs. Finally, South ruffs a heart in dummy. Now he can cash the ten of diamonds to get rid of his last heart.

This assures the contract and a beaming partner. Well worth an extra moment of thought.

Inadvertently, West can defeat the contract by returning the ten instead of a low club at the third trick. This removes an entry from dummy before South can make effective use of it. Should West see this? Probably only if he's a certified genius.

Exception to Rule Would Save the Day

"There is wickedness abroad, Watson," said Sherlock Holmes as he reached into his pocket for the handcuffs he always carried. The great detective had just watched his hand when his alert eye spotted a crime.

South dealer   **Both sides vulnerable**

```
                       NORTH
                    ♠ Q 7
                    ♡ 6 5
                    ◇ A Q 10 8 5 4
                    ♣ Q 10 5

      WEST                          EAST
   ♠ J 10 9 8 6                  ♠ K 5 2
   ♡ Q 10 7 3                    ♡ 8 4 2
   ◇ K 2                         ◇ J 9 6
   ♣ K 3                         ♣ 8 7 6 2

                    SOUTH-D
                 ♠ A 4 3
                 ♡ A K J 9
                 ◇ 7 3
                 ♣ A J 9 4
```

Defense Tricks:

☐ ☐ ☐ ☐ ☐ ☐ ☐ ☐ ☐ ☐ ☐ ☐ ☐

Bid the hand your way:

North	East	South	West
_____	_____	_____	_____
_____	_____	_____	_____
_____	_____	_____	_____
		_____	

Opening Lead _____

How the hand was bid:

SOUTH	WEST	NORTH	EAST
1 NT	Pass	3 NT	All Pass

Opening lead — ♠ J

How the hand was played: West led the jack of spades, declarer put up dummy's queen and East covered with the king. South refused the first and second spade tricks but had to win the third.

South next led a diamond, finessing with dummy's ten. East won with the jack of diamonds and returned a club. South put up the ace of clubs and led another diamond.

When the king of diamonds appeared, South ran his nine tricks—five diamonds, two hearts and the two black aces.

PICK THE CRIMINAL

While Holmes is snapping on the bracelets, pick the criminal for yourself. Read on only after you have made up your mind.

The crime occurred when South led the first diamond from his hand. West must step up with the king of diamonds—or be branded a criminal.

Declarer cannot afford to let West hold the king of diamonds, for then West would defeat the contract with the rest of the spades. But if declarer takes the first diamond trick in dummy, he cannot bring the rest of the suit in.

It costs West nothing to make the play, for his king of diamonds is clearly useless when dummy holds the A-Q. The king serves only to prevent South from ducking the first round of diamonds.

"Second hand low" is a good rule, but there are exceptions to all bridge rules.

Nuisance Overcall Proves Boomerang

The danger of making a "nuisance" overcall is that the information you give the opponents may be more valuable than anything you can tell your partner. That was the case in this hand, played in a recent rubber bridge game.

South dealer   **Both sides vulnerable**

NORTH
- ♠ A K 6
- ♡ Q 10 8 7
- ◇ A K 7 3 2
- ♣ J

WEST
- ♠ Q 10 9 7 2
- ♡ 5 2
- ◇ 9 5
- ♣ A Q 10 4

EAST
- ♠ 8
- ♡ 4 3
- ◇ Q J 10 6
- ♣ 9 8 6 5 3 2

SOUTH-D
- ♠ J 5 4 3
- ♡ A K J 9 6
- ◇ 8 4
- ♣ K 7

Defense Tricks:

☐ ☐ ☐ ☐ ☐ ☐ ☐ ☐ ☐ ☐ ☐ ☐ ☐

Bid the hand your way:

North	East	South	West
_____	_____	_____	_____
_____	_____	_____	_____
_____	_____	_____	_____
_____	_____	_____	_____
		Opening Lead	_____

154

How the hand was bid:

SOUTH	WEST	NORTH	EAST
1 ♡	1 ♠	2 ♠	Pass
3 ♡	Pass	4 ◇	Pass
4 ♡	Pass	4 NT	Pass
5 ◇	Pass	6 ♡	All Pass

Opening lead — ◇ 9

How the hand was played: It's hard to see what West hoped to accomplish with his sketchy spade overcall. Not only did he fail to talk the opponents out of a slam, but he also told South how to play the hand successfully.

West opened the nine of diamonds, and South saw the danger of losing a spade and a club. If West had not bid, South would have planned to lead a club from dummy in the hope that East had the ace of clubs. If so, South would be able to discard dummy's low spade on the king of clubs.

The bidding told South that West had the ace of clubs. The normal play could not work, and South had to look for an abnormal way to make his slam.

SETS OF DIAMONDS

Declarer took the top diamonds, ruffed a diamond high, led a trump to dummy's seven and ruffed another diamond high. Then he led a trump to dummy's ten and cashed the last diamond.

On the last diamond, South was careful to make the right discard—the seven of clubs! Declarer next cashed the king of spades, just in case East had the singleton queen. When nothing juicy fell, South led the jack of clubs from dummy.

West had to win with the ace of clubs and could not make a safe return. If West returned a spade, South would get a trick with the jack of spades. If West returned a club, South would ruff while dummy discarded the low spade. Either way the slam was home.

Keep Dummy in Line by Counting Points

Always count the points in dummy before you begin to play the hand. When you fail to make the contract, you can complain if your partner didn't have enough points for his bids. This will keep your partner strictly in line.

North dealer   **Both sides vulnerable**

	NORTH-D
	♠ Q J 10
	♡ K J 9 6
	◊ A K 7
	♣ J 10 9

WEST	EAST
♠ K 4	♠ 5 3 2
♡ 10 7 5 4	♡ Q 8
◊ Q J 10 6	◊ 9 8 5 3 2
♣ Q 5 2	♣ 8 7 3

	SOUTH
	♠ A 9 8 7 6
	♡ A 3 2
	◊ 4
	♣ A K 6 4

Defense Tricks:

☐ ☐ ☐ ☐ ☐ ☐ ☐ ☐ ☐ ☐ ☐ ☐ ☐ ☐

Bid the hand your way:

North	East	South	West
___	___	___	___
___	___	___	___
___	___	___	___
___	___	___	___
		Opening Lead ___	

156

How the hand was bid:

NORTH	EAST	SOUTH	WEST
1 NT	Pass	3 ♠	Pass
4 ♠	Pass	6 ♠	All Pass

Opening lead — ◇ Q

How the hand was played: Declarer took the first trick with dummy's king of diamonds and tried the trump finesse, losing to the king. Back came a diamond, and declarer won in dummy with the ace, discarding a heart from his hand.

South drew trumps ending in dummy, and led the jack of clubs for a finesse. This lost to the queen, and South was down one.

"You had only 15 points for your opening notrump," South complained. "I'd have made the slam if you held the queen of clubs instead of the jack."

It was true, but North's opening bid was perfectly sound. South should make the slam despite the bad breaks in the black suits.

RUFF DIAMOND

The first two tricks were correct, but South should not win the second diamond in dummy. Instead, he should play low from dummy and ruff in his hand.

South draws trumps and cashes the ace and king of hearts. If nothing startling happens in hearts, South is in position to discard a heart on the ace of diamonds and then lead the jack of clubs for a finessee. It therefore costs nothing to try the hearts first.

Actually, the queen of hearts would drop. Now South gets to his hand with the king of clubs to lead his third heart. A finesse gives him two tricks with dummy's J-9 of hearts. South discards one club on the extra heart and the other low club on dummy's ace of diamonds.

If South plays the hand properly, he can then congratulate his partner on bidding one notrump with only 15 points.

157

Forget Old Rules in Modern Bridge

Most bridge players follow the old rule of drawing trumps immediately under the impression that this is as unchangeable as the laws of the ancient Medes and Persians. Modern experts have discovered that one man's Mede is another man's Persian.

South dealer   **North-South vulnerable**

NORTH
♠ A Q 10 9 2
♡ A 7
◇ K Q J 5
♣ Q 7

WEST   EAST
♠ 6 3   ♠ K J 8 5
♡ 8 2   ♡ 6 5 3
◇ A 10 9 8   ◇ 7 2
♣ J 10 9 6 2   ♣ 8 5 4 3

SOUTH-D
♠ 7 4
♡ K Q J 10 9 4
◇ 6 4 3
♣ A K

Defense Tricks:

☐ ☐ ☐ ☐ ☐ ☐ ☐ ☐ ☐ ☐ ☐ ☐

Bid the hand your way:

North	East	South	West
_____	_____	_____	_____
_____	_____	_____	_____
_____	_____	_____	_____
_____	_____	_____	_____

Opening Lead _____

How the hand was bid:

SOUTH	WEST	NORTH	EAST
1 ♡	Pass	2 ♠	Pass
3 ♡	Pass	4 ◇	Pass
4 ♡	Pass	5 ♡	Pass
6 ♡	All Pass		

Opening lead — ♣ J

How the hand was played: South won the first trick with the king of clubs and followed the old rule by drawing trumps at once. Then he led a diamond to dummy's king.

South got back with the ace of clubs to lead another diamond. West ducked again, and dummy's queen won. Now South could not get to his hand to lead his last diamond toward dummy.

Declarer led the low diamond from dummy in the hope that the ace would fall. It didn't. West shifted to a spade, and the finesse lost to the king. South was down one—all because he had followed an old rule blindly.

SMALL RISK

South should lead the six of diamonds at the second trick. There is only a very small risk that a defender can get a quick ruff. It is far more likely that declarer will be allowed to win the first trick in dummy with the king.

Now South can afford to draw three rounds of trumps. He is in position to lead a second diamond to dummy's queen. He gets back with the ace of clubs to lead a third diamond, and West must take the ace.

Declarer gets to dummy with the ace of spades to discard his other spade on the jack of diamonds. There is no further problem.

The trouble with drawing trumps immediately is that this removes an easy way of getting from the dummy to the South hand. Do your planning before you draw trumps because it may turn out that you don't want to draw the trumps after all.

Full Rule Is Worth Following

According to the latest statistics, a bridge player makes a disastrous mistake every fifteen seconds. With your luck, that player will be your partner. Strangely enough, some of the worst disasters take place when a player thinks he is following the "rules" for good play.

South dealer   **North-South vulnerable**

```
                        NORTH
                        ♠ Q J 10 9 6
                        ♡ 10 2
                        ◊ 7 5
                        ♣ A 6 5 3

        WEST                            EAST
        ♠ 4 2                           ♠ K 8 7 5 3
        ♡ 7 6 3                         ♡ 5 4
        ◊ Q J 9 4                       ◊ K 8 6
        ♣ K J 7 2                       ♣ 9 8 4

                        SOUTH-D
                        ♠ A
                        ♡ A K Q J 9 8
                        ◊ A 10 3 2
                        ♣ Q 10
```

Defense Tricks:

☐ ☐ ☐ ☐ ☐ ☐ ☐ ☐ ☐ ☐ ☐ ☐ ☐

Bid the hand your way:

North	East	South	West
_____	_____	_____	_____
_____	_____	_____	_____
_____	_____	_____	_____
_____	_____	_____	_____

Opening Lead _____

160

How the hand was bid:

SOUTH	WEST	NORTH	WEST
2 ♡	Pass	2 ♠	Pass
3 ◇	Pass	3 ♡	Pass
5 ♡	Pass	6 ♡	All Pass

Opening lead — ◇ Q

How the hand was played: South took his three aces and led a trump to dummy's ten. He then led the queen of spades from dummy for a ruffing finesse.

"Cover an honor with an honor," East muttered as he played the king of spades.

South delightedly ruffed the king of spades, drew the last trump and got to dummy with a club to discard three losers on the rest of the good spades. Game, slam and rubber were very satisfactory to North and South

DIDN'T KNOW

East didn't know the full rule: Cover an honor with an honor only if this will set up a trick for you or for your partner.

In this case, South had gone to the trouble of cashing the ace of spades before leading the queen of spades from dummy. Obviously South was out of spades and East could not possibly set up a defensive trick by covering with the king.

East should play a low spade, allowing South to discard a diamond. Declarer continues with dummy's jack of spades, and East plays low again. South throws another diamond, and West comes to the rescue by ruffing.

West leads a diamond to the king, defeating the contract, and the defenders eventually get a club trick to collect an additional 100 points.

Comfort Partner with Important Words

The most important two words in a bridge player's vocabulary are "Very unlucky." Use them when your partner finds a way to go down at an ice-cold contract.

South dealer   **Both sides vulnerable**

NORTH
♠ 10 9 8 4
♡ A K 6
♢ K 8 4
♣ K 5 2

WEST	EAST
♠ K 5	♠ 7 3
♡ Q J 10 8 4 2	♡ 9
♢ Q 10 5	♢ J 9 7 2
♣ 10 6	♣ Q J 9 8 4 3

SOUTH-D
♠ A Q J 6 2
♡ 7 5 3
♢ A 6 3
♣ A 7

Defense Tricks:

☐ ☐ ☐ ☐ ☐ ☐ ☐ ☐ ☐ ☐ ☐ ☐ ☐

Bid the hand your way:

North	East	South	West
_____	_____	_____	_____
_____	_____	_____	_____
_____	_____	_____	_____
_____	_____	_____	_____
		Opening Lead	_____

How the hand was bid:

SOUTH	WEST	NORTH	EAST
1 ♠	Pass	3 ♠	Pass
4 ♠	All Pass		

Opening lead — ♡ Q

How the hand was played: Put yourself in the North seat in this hand. You are the dummy, anxiously watching your partner play the hand at four spades.

West opens the queen of hearts, and your partner wins in dummy with the king. He leads the ten of trumps from dummy, and East plays low. You keep a brave smile on your face as you watch your partner go through the process that he calls "thinking."

Finally, your partner plays a low trump from his hand. West wins with the king of trumps and leads the jack of hearts. Your partner puts up dummy's ace of hearts, and East ruffs.

REPEAT PHRASE

Your partner's face falls, and you murmur a comforting "Very unlucky." Your partner struggles through the hand, going down one, and you repeat the magic phrase.

The idea is to keep your partner in good spirits, Maybe he will play the next hand merely badly instead of disastrously.

You could point out that East's nine of hearts on the first trick should have warned your partner of the danger of a ruff. You could observe that the contract is unbeatable if your partner takes the ace of trumps and leads another trump instead of trying a trump finesse.

You could win the argument and lose a partner. Stick to "Very unlucky" and you'll have happier partners and better scores.

Play "Discovered" Twenty Years Ago

"There is no such thing as a new play," Sonny Moyse remarked to me twenty years ago, "but I've never read anything about a play I made last night." Moyse was the editor of the **Bridge World** Magazine and wrote about his discovery, but his play is still unknown except to a handful of experts.

North dealer   **North-South vulnerable**

NORTH-D
♠ K 10 9
♡ 4 2
♢ Q J 10 9 2
♣ A Q J

WEST   **EAST**
♠ 8 6 5 2   ♠ 7 4 3
♡ 5 3   ♡ K Q J 9 8
♢ K 8   ♢ A 7 4
♣ 7 6 4 3 2   ♣ 8 5

SOUTH
♠ A Q J
♡ A 10 7 6
♢ 6 5 3
♣ K 10 9

Defense Tricks:

☐ ☐ ☐ ☐ ☐ ☐ ☐ ☐ ☐ ☐ ☐ ☐ ☐

Bid the hand your way:

North	East	South	West
————	————	————	————
————	————	————	————
————	————	————	————
————	————	————	————
		Opening Lead	————

164

How the hand was bid:

NORTH	EAST	SOUTH	WEST
1 ◇	1 ♡	2 NT	Pass
3 NT	All Pass		

Opening lead — ♡ 5

How the hand was played: When West opened the five of hearts, Moyse could see that South held all of the higher hearts—the A-10-7-6. Which card should Moyse play from the East hand at the first trick?

The "book" play is the jack of hearts. South refuses the trick. If East continues with the king of hearts, South holds off again. East next leads a low heart, and South wins with the ten.

When South leads the diamonds, West can win the first diamond but cannot return a heart. South wins any return and knocks out the ace of diamonds. South gets back with the ace of hearts to take the rest.

If East wins the first diamond, he can set up the hearts but can never get back to cash them. South loses only two diamonds and two hearts either way.

LOOKS AHEAD

Moyse looked ahead to see all this and therefore played the eight of hearts at the first trick. South had to win with the ten.

When South led a diamond, West stepped up with the king of diamonds to lead his other heart. This set up the rest of East's suit. When East got in with the ace of diamonds, he cashed the rest of the hearts to defeat the contract.

South has two sure heart tricks no matter how East defends. East must prevent South from refusing the first trick so that West will be able to lead another heart when he wins the first diamond.

Criminal Detected after Hand

"I'm going to catch the culprit tonight," Sherlock Holmes remarked to Dr. Watson as they entered the bridge club. "One of the players is counterfeiting Confederate money." The great detective caught the criminal after watching this hand.

East dealer   **Both sides vulnerable**

NORTH
♠ K 9 8 7 2
♡ 6 2
♢ A J 6
♣ A 10 5

WEST   EAST-D
♠ 5 3   ♠ 6
♡ 10   ♡ A Q J 9 8 4
♢ 9 8 5 4 3 2   ♢ K Q 10
♣ Q J 7 6   ♣ K 9 4

SOUTH
♠ A Q J 10 4
♡ K 7 5 3
♢ 7
♣ 8 3 2

Defense Tricks:

□ □ □ □ □ □ □ □ □ □ □ □ □

Bid the hand your way:

North	East	South	West
———	———	———	———
———	———	———	———
———	———	———	———
———	———	———	———

Opening Lead _____

166

How the hand was bid:

EAST	SOUTH	WEST	NORTH
1 ♡	1 ♠	Pass	4 ♠
All Pass			

Opening lead — ♡ 10

How the hand was played: East won the first trick with the ace of hearts and returned the queen. West ruffed the king of hearts and returned a diamond. Declarer won with dummy's ace of diamonds and drew trumps.

South eventually lost two club tricks, going down one. Sherlock Holmes then produced a pair of handcuffs and took the criminal off to jail.

Who was the criminal, and how did Sherlock Holmes know that he was the counterfeiter? Decide for yourself before you read on.

WOEFUL MISPLAY

South misplayed the hand woefully. He should play a low heart on East's queen at the second trick, thus allowing East to win.

If East leads a third heart, South must play low from his hand and ruff in the dummy. The idea is to save the king of hearts so that South can eventually win a trick with it.

Declarer then draws trumps and leads the king of hearts to discard a club from the dummy. This limits the club loss to one trick. South loses only one club and two hearts, making game and rubber.

Sherlock Holmes put the handcuffs on East because he noticed that East's pockets were full of counterfeit Confederate money. Holmes was too wise a bird to think that South was a criminal just because he played bad bridge. If we put all the bad bridge players behind bars, the rest of us would die of loneliness.

Cartoon Characters Muff Game Contract

In cartoons, but not in real life, a man sometimes paints himself into an exitless corner of a room. Don't laugh too hard; you wouldn't do it yourself at the bridge table, but your partner does it all the time.

South dealer   **Both sides vulnerable**

NORTH
- ♠ Q 10 6
- ♡ 10 6 4
- ◇ K Q J 7 4
- ♣ Q 7

WEST
- ♠ K 4
- ♡ 8
- ◇ 10 5 3 2
- ♣ K J 9 6 3 2

EAST
- ♠ 8 5 3 2
- ♡ Q J 9 7 3
- ◇ A
- ♣ 10 5 4

SOUTH-D
- ♠ A J 9 7
- ♡ A K 5 2
- ◇ 9 8 6
- ♣ A 8

Defense Tricks:

Bid the hand your way:

North	East	South	West
_____	_____	_____	_____
_____	_____	_____	_____
_____	_____	_____	_____
_____	_____	_____	_____

Opening Lead _____

How the hand was bid:

SOUTH	WEST	NORTH	EAST
1 NT	Pass	3 NT	All Pass

Opening lead — ♣ 6

How the hand was played: Your partner is declarer at three notrump. He wins the first trick in dummy with the queen of clubs (sighing with relief), gets to his hand with a heart and leads the six of diamonds toward dummy.

Since South cannot see through the backs of the cards, he plays the jack from dummy to force out the ace, wins the club return and leads the eight of diamonds to dummy's queen. East discards a spade, and South sees that he is in trouble.

If South tries the spade finesse, it will lose. If he gets to his hand with a heart to lead the nine of diamonds, West will play low. South can stay in his hand with the nine of diamonds or overtake with dummy's king, but he cannot run the rest of the suit.

This is a good time to laugh, if you happen to be in the mood. The opponents will join you.

MUST UNBLOCK

Since you are not a cartoon character, you would unblock the diamonds. You begin by leading the nine of diamonds. Dummy's jack loses to the ace; you win the club return and lead the eight to dummy's queen. East's spade discard tells you that West still has the 10-5 of diamonds.

You get to your hand with a heart to lead the carefully preserved six of diamonds. West plays low, and you overtake with dummy's seven. Now you are in dummy and can continue with the king of diamonds and then the last diamond. You score game and rubber with four diamonds, two clubs, two hearts and one spade.

169

Don't Be Content with Half Loaf

People keep telling us that half a loaf is better than none, and they're quite right. They forget to point out that three-quarters of a loaf is better than half.

North dealer   **North-South vulnerable**

NORTH-D
- ♠ K Q J 8
- ♡ J 8 7 3
- ◇ A 3
- ♣ A J 2

WEST
- ♠ 10 7 6 2
- ♡ Q 6 4
- ◇ K 10 4
- ♣ 10 7 3

EAST
- ♠ 9 5 4 3
- ♡ 9
- ◇ J 9 8 7 6
- ♣ Q 8 4

SOUTH
- ♠ A
- ♡ A K 10 5 2
- ◇ Q 5 2
- ♣ K 9 6 5

Defense Tricks:

☐ ☐ ☐ ☐ ☐ ☐ ☐ ☐ ☐ ☐ ☐ ☐ ☐

Bid the hand your way:

North	East	South	West
___	___	___	___
___	___	___	___
___	___	___	___
___	___	___	___
		Opening Lead ___	

How the hand was bid:

NORTH	EAST	SOUTH	WEST
1 NT	Pass	3 ♡	Pass
4 ♡	Pass	6 ♡	All Pass

Opening lead — ♠ 2

How the hand was played: South took the ace of spades and led out the ace and king of trumps. When the queen of hearts failed to drop, South cashed the king of clubs and tried a finesse with dummy's jack of clubs. This gave him a 50 percent chance for the slam, but it turned out to be not enough.

South's best chance for the contract was to make West open the clubs. Then the slam would come home not only if West had the queen but also if West had the ten of clubs. The odds were 3 to 1 that West held at least one of the missing club honors so that the right line of play would give declarer a three-quarter chance.

END PLAY

After taking the top trumps, South should lead a diamond to dummy and cash the rest of the spades, discarding two diamonds and a club. Then declarer ruffs dummy's low diamond and gives West his trump trick.

West cannot return a diamond since dummy would ruff while South tossed another club. Instead, West returns a low club.

South plays low from dummy, and as the cards lie East's queen is trapped. If East had the ten of clubs and could play it to escape the trap, South could still try a finesse with dummy's jack of clubs. He thus gets two plays in clubs instead of only one.

Make Resolution to Play Generously

There is always time to make a resolution for the New Year: Be generous to your opponents. Give them a trick they don't expect to win. And don't forget that a new year begins every day.

South dealer   **East-West vulnerable**

NORTH
♠ A 8 5 3 2
♡ A 10 9 8
◊ 7 3
♣ Q 5

WEST   EAST
♠ J 10 9 6   ♠ K Q
♡ 4   ♡ None
◊ A 9 8 4   ◊ Q J 10 6 2
♣ A K 9 6   ♣ J 10 8 4 3 2

SOUTH-D
♠ 7 4
♡ K Q J 7 6 5 3 2
◊ K 5
♣ 7

Defense Tricks:

☐ ☐ ☐ ☐ ☐ ☐ ☐ ☐ ☐ ☐ ☐ ☐ ☐

Bid the hand your way:

North	East	South	West
_____	_____	_____	_____
_____	_____	_____	_____
_____	_____	_____	_____
_____	_____	_____	_____
		Opening Lead	_____

How the hand was bid:

SOUTH	WEST	NORTH	EAST
4 ♡	All Pass		

Opening lead — ♣ K

How the hand was played: If you played this sort of hand last year, you ruffed the second club, drew trumps and tried to develop the spades. East got in with a high spade to lead the queen of diamonds through your king. The defenders got one club, one spade and two diamonds, defeating your contract.

Of course you gloated quietly and modestly about this triumph because the opponents could have made a slam in diamonds or clubs if you hadn't shut them out by bidding four hearts.

This year give yourself a real chance to gloat by making your contract. Let West take the second trick with the ace of clubs. Throw away a spade instead of trumping the second round of clubs.

ONLY EXCHANGE

This looks very generous, but it is really just an exchange of tricks. You have given up a club trick instead of a spade. A little string is tied to your gift.

If West leads a trump at the third trick (his best defense), you win, take the ace of spades and ruff a spade. You lead a trump to dummy's nine to ruff another spade and lead another trump to dummy's ten to ruff yet another spade.

By this time, dummy's last spade is good. You lead a trump to dummy's ace and throw a diamond on that good spade. Now you lose only one diamond trick, and you therefore make four hearts. A good way to start a year.

Charge of Murder May Be Too Strong

The average bridge player is not a deliberate murderer. I am ready to go to court to testify that there cannot be malice aforethought where there has been no thought.

South dealer   **North-South vulnerable**

NORTH
- ♠ 6 4
- ♡ A K 7 6
- ◊ K 5
- ♣ Q 9 7 6 4

WEST
- ♠ K J 10 8 7
- ♡ 8 3 2
- ◊ A J 10 9
- ♣ 10

EAST
- ♠ 9 5 3 2
- ♡ 5
- ◊ 8 7 6 3 2
- ♣ K J 8

SOUTH-D
- ♠ A Q
- ♡ Q J 10 9 4
- ◊ Q 4
- ♣ A 5 3 2

Defense Tricks:

☐ ☐ ☐ ☐ ☐ ☐ ☐ ☐ ☐ ☐ ☐ ☐ ☐

Bid the hand your way:

North	East	South	West
_____	_____	_____	_____
_____	_____	_____	_____
_____	_____	_____	_____
_____	_____	_____	_____

Opening Lead _____

How the hand was bid:

SOUTH	WEST	NORTH	EAST
1 ♡	1 ♠	3 ♡	Pass
4 ♡	All Pass		

Opening lead — ♣ 10

How the hand was played: When this hand was played, for example, South murdered his contract at the very first trick, but nobody can possibly believe that thought had anything to do with the case. West led the ten of clubs, and declarer played the queen of clubs from dummy.

South's contract groaned and died right then, but South didn't find out about it until a few tricks later.

East put up the king of clubs at the first trick, and South won with the ace. Declarer drew trumps and led a club, losing to East's eight. Back came a spade, and South had to try the finesse. The defenders thus got two clubs, one spade and one diamond.

OBVIOUS LEAD

If South thinks about the opening lead, he must realize that the ten of clubs is either a singleton or the top of the doubleton 10-8. In either case, it cannot do any good to play the queen of clubs from dummy.

If South plays low from dummy at the first trick, East follows with the eight. South plays low. South knows he must lose two club tricks, but he wants to lose one of them to West rather than to East.

Since West cannot safely lead spades, he switches to a trump. South draws trumps, takes the ace of clubs and gives up a club. Now when East leads a spade, South does not need the finesse. He takes the ace of spades and runs the last two clubs, discarding the queen of spades on dummy's fifth club.

Keep Eyes on Dangerous Opponent

If you suspect that somebody may be getting ready to conk you over the noggin, keep an eye on the fellow with his hands behind his back. You don't have to worry about the gent with the empty hands.

South dealer   **Neither side vulnerable**

NORTH
♠ Q 9 6 3
♡ A 4 3
♢ A 10 5
♣ J 10 4

WEST
♠ None
♡ 10 7 5
♢ K J 8 7 6 2
♣ A K 7 3

EAST
♠ A 10 8 4
♡ 8 2
♢ 9 4
♣ Q 9 8 6 5

SOUTH-D
♠ K J 7 5 2
♡ K Q J 9 6
♢ Q 3
♣ 2

Defense Tricks:

☐ ☐ ☐ ☐ ☐ ☐ ☐ ☐ ☐ ☐ ☐ ☐ ☐

Bid the hand your way:

North	East	South	West
_____	_____	_____	_____
_____	_____	_____	_____
_____	_____	_____	_____
		_____	

Opening Lead _____

176

How the hand was bid:

SOUTH	WEST	NORTH	EAST
1 ♠	2 ◇	3 ♠	Pass
4 ♠	All Pass		

Opening lead — ♣ K

How the hand was played: West opened the king of clubs and continued with the ace. South ruffed and saw that the hand was a piece of cake if trumps broke normally. The trouble was that one opponent might hold all the missing trumps.

There was no need to worry about West. From the lead it was clear that West had started with at least three clubs. From the bidding it was a cinch that West held at least six diamonds. There wasn't room in West's hand for as many as four spades.

There was plenty of room in the East hand, so South took the precaution of starting the trumps by leading low from his own hand. West discarded a diamond, and dummy's queen forced out the ace. South had kept his eye on the dangerous opponent.

CONTINUES CLUBS

East continued with the queen of clubs, and South threw away a diamond. He could not afford to ruff in his own hand and then draw trumps.

East continued with a fourth club (the best defense), and dummy ruffed. Declarer led the nine of spades from dummy, East covered with the ten and South won with the jack. Declarer then got to dummy with the ace of hearts to lead the six of spades from dummy.

No matter what East did, South was sure to win the next two tricks with the king and seven of trumps. Then declarer could take the rest of the tricks with good hearts and the ace of diamonds.

Tournament Expert Shows Right Play

The chief feature of tournament bridge is that the same hand is played at more than one table. If you miss the key play at your table, your partner is sure to notice the difference in the score at another table, and he will tell you what a fine play the other fellow made.

West dealer   **East-West vulnerable**

NORTH
♠ A K 6 3
♡ J 9 4
♢ A 7 5
♣ Q 6 2

WEST-D   EAST
♠ 9   ♠ 8 5 2
♡ A K Q 7 6   ♡ 5
♢ K J 10 4   ♢ 9 6 3 2
♣ A J 9   ♣ 10 8 7 4 3

SOUTH
♠ Q J 10 7 4
♡ 10 8 3 2
♢ Q 8
♣ K 5

Defense Tricks:

☐ ☐ ☐ ☐ ☐ ☐ ☐ ☐ ☐ ☐ ☐ ☐ ☐

Bid the hand your way:

North	East	South	West
_____	_____	_____	_____
_____	_____	_____	_____
_____	_____	_____	_____
_____	_____	_____	_____

Opening Lead _____

How the hand was bid:

WEST	NORTH	EAST	SOUTH
1 ♡	Pass	Pass	1 ♠
Double	Redouble	2 ♣	Pass
Pass	3 ♠	All Pass	
			Opening lead — ♡ K

How the hand was played: When this hand was played in the 1966 team Selection Tournament in Pittsburgh, the final contract was three spades at most tables. In most cases West took three top hearts and then led a fourth heart.

Declarer ruffed the fourth heart with dummy's ace of trumps, led a spade to the queen and then returned a low club.

West could not afford to step up with the ace since then South would eventually discard a diamond on dummy's queen of clubs. When West played a low club, dummy won with the queen. South then led out the rest of his trumps.

THROWN IN

Declarer, West and dummy each kept one club and two diamonds. South then led a club, throwing West into the lead. West had to return a diamond, and South let this ride around to his queen.

It all looked very normal at the time, but when all the scores were put up, each West saw that one East had managed to defeat the contract. Each West then casually mentioned the right play to his partner.

The successful East was Bob Hamman, Los Angeles expert. His partner, Lew Mathe, started with the king and queen of hearts, followed by the ace of hearts. Hamman trumped his partner's ace!

Hamman then returned a diamond, and South was dead. Whenever South led a club, West could take the ace of clubs and a diamond trick to defeat the contract.

Don't Hope for More Than You Really Need

Sometimes you can make a hand against any possible break, but more often you must hope that the missing cards will break reasonably. Keep your hopes to the bare minimum; it's foolish to lose your contract because you asked for more than you really needed.

North dealer   **Both sides vulnerable**

NORTH-D
♠ 10 6 2
♡ A J
♦ A 6
♣ K J 9 7 6 3

WEST
♠ 9 5
♡ K 10 9 6 3
♦ Q 10 5 2
♣ 8 2

EAST
♠ Q J 7
♡ Q 8 7 2
♦ J 8
♣ A Q 10 4

SOUTH
♠ A K 8 4 3
♡ 5 4
♦ K 9 7 4 3
♣ 5

Defense Tricks:

☐ ☐ ☐ ☐ ☐ ☐ ☐ ☐ ☐ ☐ ☐ ☐ ☐

Bid the hand your way:

North	East	South	West
___	___	___	___
___	___	___	___
___	___	___	___
___	___	___	___
		Opening Lead ___	

How the hand was bid:

NORTH	EAST	SOUTH	WEST
1 ♣	Pass	1 ♠	Pass
2 ♣	Pass	2 ◇	Pass
2 NT	Pass	3 ◇	Pass
3 ♠	Pass	4 ♠	All Pass

Opening lead — ♡ 10

How the hand was played: Declarer took the first trick with dummy's ace of hearts, cashed the top diamonds and ruffed a diamond with the ten of spades. East overruffed, led a heart to the king and overruffed dummy again on a diamond return.

East then returned his last trump and sat tight until he got the setting trick with the ace of clubs.

South would have made his contract if the diamonds had broken 3-3 or if East had been unable to get two diamond ruffs. He didn't need this kind of luck. He was safe even if the diamonds broke 4-2.

FAIR EXCHANGE

It was correct to take the ace of hearts and the top diamonds. When South next leads a low diamond, however, he should discard dummy's jack of hearts instead of ruffing.

This gives the opponents their diamond trick at the expense of a heart trick that they were surely going to take. If West leads another diamond, East can overruff dummy, but this costs him his sure trump trick.

At this stage, the defenders have taken one diamond and one trump. They will eventually get their ace of clubs, but nothing else. Whenever South regains the lead he can ruff a heart in dummy and draw trumps with the ace and king.

Crime Doesn't Pay at Table

"A sad case, Watson," said Sherlock Holmes. "We came too late to stop the crime." The great detective and his biographer had arrived just as this bridge hand was being played.

South dealer   **Both sides vulnerable**

```
                    NORTH
                 ♠ Q J 10 9
                 ♡ A J 8
                 ◇ 7 4 3
                 ♣ 9 4 3
      WEST                      EAST
   ♠ K 8 6                   ♠ 5
   ♡ 9 4                     ♡ 10 6 5 3 2
   ◇ K Q 2                   ◇ 9 8 6 5
   ♣ Q J 10 6 2              ♣ K 8 7
                   SOUTH-D
                 ♠ A 7 4 3 2
                 ♡ K Q 7
                 ◇ A J 10
                 ♣ A 5
```

Defense Tricks:

☐ ☐ ☐ ☐ ☐ ☐ ☐ ☐ ☐ ☐ ☐ ☐ ☐

Bid the hand your way:

North	East	South	West
———	———	———	———
———	———	———	———
———	———	———	———
———	———	———	———

Opening Lead ———

182

How the hand was bid:

SOUTH	WEST	NORTH	EAST
1 ♠	Pass	2 ♠	Pass
4 ♠	All Pass		

Opening lead — ♣ Q

How the hand was played: They saw South win the first trick with the ace of clubs and enter dummy with the jack of hearts to lead the queen of spades. West took the king of spades and returned the six of clubs to East's king.

East returned the nine of diamonds, and South tried a finesse with the ten. This lost to the queen, and South ruffed the club return. Declarer drew trumps and tried another diamond finesse, going down one when this finesse lost also.

If you study the evidence, you will know who committed the crime. While you're getting the handcuffs ready, decide for yourself what the crime was and who committed it. Then read on.

EARLY CRIME

The handcuffs belong on South's wrists since he should have made his contract of four spades. South's crime occurred at the very first trick, when he took the ace of clubs. The correct play is to refuse the first trick.

This simple maneuver keeps East out of the lead. West leads another club to the ace, South gets to dummy with the jack of hearts and a spade finesse loses to the king.

West returns a heart to the king; South draws two more trumps, ruffs dummy's last club and leads a heart to the ace. Then he leads a diamond from dummy, finessing with the ten.

West wins but cannot get out safely. If West returns a diamond, South gets a free finesse. If West returns anything else, dummy ruffs while South discards the jack of diamonds.

Case History Tells Grim Tragedy

The trouble with going out at night is that your children may be brought up by bad bridge players. A man may be handicapped all his life because a nurse taught him to take an ace whenever he got the chance.

North dealer   **Both sides vulnerable**

NORTH-D
- ♠ A 7
- ♡ 8
- ◇ K 7 5 3 2
- ♣ 10 8 7 6 3

WEST
- ♠ K Q J 9
- ♡ 10 9 4
- ◇ 9 8 4
- ♣ A Q 2

EAST
- ♠ 10 8 6 5
- ♡ 7 3
- ◇ Q J 10 6
- ♣ K J 4

SOUTH
- ♠ 4 3 2
- ♡ A K Q J 6 5 2
- ◇ A
- ♣ 9 5

Defense Tricks:

☐ ☐ ☐ ☐ ☐ ☐ ☐ ☐ ☐ ☐ ☐ ☐ ☐

Bid the hand your way:

North	East	South	West
_____	_____	_____	_____
_____	_____	_____	_____
_____	_____	_____	_____
_____	_____	_____	_____

Opening Lead _____

How the hand was bid:

NORTH	EAST	SOUTH	WEST
Pass	Pass	4 ♡	All Pass

Opening lead — ♠ K

How the hand was played: This hand comes from the files of a Beverly Hills psychiatrist with the consent of the patient, now healthy and sane—if you can use those words in describing a television producer. Patient A.G. played the hand in his ace-grabbing days.

West led the king of spades, and our patient took the ace at once. He cashed the ace of diamonds and led another spade, hoping to ruff his third spade in dummy. East returned a trump, of course, and South eventually lost two spades and two clubs.

HEALTHY COMMENT

"I wouldn't play the hand that way anymore," a healthy A.G. comments. "I would just refuse to win the first trick with the ace of spades."

That assures the contract. If the defenders take two clubs and then lead a spade, South can ruff his third spade in dummy. If they lead a trump instead of a spade, South draws trumps and clears the ace of diamonds out of the way. Then he leads a spade to dummy's ace and discards the last spade on the king of diamonds.

"Playing an ace too quickly is a symptom of regressive hostility coupled with a tendency toward dandruff," comments the psychiatrist, closing his file on A.G.

A man can't be too careful.